Science
Uncovered

AQA
Additional
Science
for GCSE

Revision guide

Ben Clyde

Series Editor:
Keith Hirst

Heinemann

From Harcourt

Heinemann Educational Publishers
Halley Court, Jordan Hill, Oxford OX2 8EJ
Part of Harcourt Education

Heinemann is the registered trademark of
Harcourt Education Limited

© Harcourt Education Limited 2007

First published 2007

11 10 09 08 07
10 9 8 7 6 5 4 3 2 1

British Library Cataloguing in Publication Data is available from
the British Library on request.

10-digit ISBN: 0 435675 53 2
13-digit ISBN: 978 0 435675 53 0

Designed by Ken Vail Graphic Design
Project managed, edited and typeset by Bookcraft Ltd
(Alex Sharpe, Project Manager)

Harcourt project team: Marcus Bell, David Cooke, Ross Laman
Andrew Halcro-Johnston, Sarah Ross, Ruth Simms, Iti Singh

Original illustrations © Harcourt Education Limited 2007

Illustrated by Beehive Illustration (Martin Sanders, Mark Turner),
Bookcraft India Pvt Ltd (Gemma Raj), Nick Hawken, NB Illustration
(Ben Hasler, Ruth Thomlevold), Sylvie Poggio Artists Agency (Rory
Walker)

Printed in Italy by Printer Trento S.r.l.

Cover photo © Superstock

Every effort has been made to contact copyright holders of
material reproduced in this book. Any omissions will be rectified
in subsequent printings if notice is given to the publishers.

Contents

How to use this book

This AQA Science Uncovered revision guide will help you revise for the AQA Additional Science exam. The guide summarises what you have learnt and links directly to the AQA Additional Science specification.

This revision guide is divided into three units: B2, C2 and P2. Each unit is broken down into separate sections. For example, B2 consists of sections 1–4.

Each section starts with a list of learning outcomes covering the key parts of the section. This will help you to focus on what you need to revise.

After revising this section, you should be able...

● to relate the structures of different types of animal and plant cell to their function

● to explain with examples how substances get into and out of cells by diffusion and osmosis

You will find in-text questions throughout the text to help you to check your understanding. Test yourself as you revise each section. If you get them all correct, move on. If not, make a note to go back and revise that section again. We have given you the answers to the questions on page 67.

Question

1 What is the overall electric charge on an atom? Explain your answer.

Key words are shown in **bold** and key equations are highlighted. The key words also appear together with a definition in a combined glossary and index at the end of the revision guide.

speed = slope of distance–time graph

The exam will ask you to incorporate ideas about 'How science works' into your answers. Parts of questions may address How science works, subject content or a blend of both. The How science works boxes will help you to apply this thinking to your answers. Remember that you should be continually questioning how scientists collect data and use evidence.

How science works

Use ideas about energy wastage to suggest why food chains rarely have more than five levels.

Page 58 gives an example of how How science works could be used during an investigation and the questions you need to think about.

Exam tips highlight common mistakes and give you advice about exam preparation so you can achieve better grades.

Exam tip

Remember: 'denature' does not mean 'kill' – it refers to a change of shape.

We have included lots of simple, full colour diagrams and concept maps to help you revise and to make the content more digestible.

The revision guide is based on the new specification and the example exam questions (page 60) will give you valuable preparation for the exam. The answers that follow allow you to check your progress and improve next time!

ISA and PSA hints and tips (page 59) is a helpful reminder of the method you should use during any investigation. This will be useful when answering questions in the exam.

Revision and exam advice

You will get the most out of this guide by using the in-text questions and exam questions to check that you understand the content. Take note of the exam tips – they will help you to avoid mistakes other students have made in the past!

You may find these revision tips useful:

- Revise regularly – do *not* leave revision until near the exam.
- Plan your revision carefully – this will help you avoid a last minute rush.
- Revise in a quiet room – you cannot revise properly with the television on or if you are listening to music.
- Revise in short stretches – work for half an hour, have a breather for ten minutes, then start again. You should be able to revise for about 2–3 hours in an evening.
- Make your revision 'active' – read a topic, then close your book and make a summary from memory. Go back and see what is missing from your summary.
- Try to get plenty of exercise and enough sleep before the exam – you will be more alert.

During the exam:

- Read the question carefully – circle the key words and make sure you know what you are being asked to do.
- Look at the number of marks allocated to decide how long to spend on a question. If three marks are given then you need to make three relevant points to gain full marks. When you are answering the example exam questions, number the points you have made '1', '2' and so on.
- Look at how much space has been left for the answer. One line means you only need to give a short answer. If there is a blank space you may be expected to draw a diagram.
- Use scientific terminology in your answers wherever possible.
- Quote the equation and show your working when doing calculations. Remember to include a unit for your answer!
- Draw diagrams and graphs carefully in pencil and label them.

Good luck with your exams!

After revising this section, you should be able...

- to relate the structures of different types of animal and plant cell to their function
- to explain with examples how substances get into and out of cells by diffusion and osmosis
- to evaluate the benefits of manipulating the environment in which we grow plants in order to maximise the rate of photosynthesis

Cells

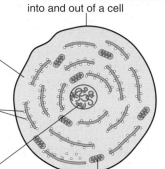

cell membrane, which controls the movement of substances into and out of a cell

the **cytoplasm** is where most of a cell's chemical reactions take place

ribosomes, where a cell makes proteins

nucleus, which contains genetic information that controls the activities of a cell

mitochondrion (plural mitochondria), where energy stored in sugars is released

▲ A typical animal cell.

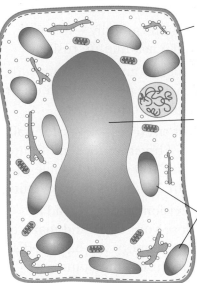

cell wall made of tiny fibres, which make a cell stronger

permanent **vacuole**, which is a space filled with a liquid called **cell sap** – this helps to support a cell

chloroplasts, which contain a green pigment called chlorophyll – this absorbs light energy, which a cell uses to make food in a series of chemical reactions called photosynthesis

▲ A typical plant cell.

Questions

1 *Copy the diagram of the plant cell and add labels showing the nucleus, cytoplasm, cell membrane, a mitochondrion and a ribosome.*
2 *Copy the table. Then close the book and fill in the blanks.*

Part of cell	Animal or plant cells?	Function
cell membrane	both	controls movement of substances into and out of cells
nucleus		
vacuole		
chloroplast		
mitochondrion		
cell wall		
ribosome		
cytoplasm		

Exam tip

Remember: many features are present in both animal and plant cells.

Specialised cells

Cells may be **specialised** to carry out a particular function. Their structure is adapted to their function.

Type of cell	Structural features	Function
xylem cells	dead cells form long, thin tubes which are rigid and waterproof	transport water and ions from roots to leaves, support the plant
phloem cells	long thin tubes	transport sugars from leaves to rest of plant
guard cells	present in pairs, can change shape	create pores in leaves that can be opened and closed for gas exchange
white blood cells	large, can change shape	ingest bacteria
muscle cells	made of fibres that can shorten and lengthen	movement
motor neurone cells	highly branched at one end, often very long	receive chemicals from relay neurones, transmit impulses over long distances
sperm cells	small and streamlined with a long, flexible tail	move to reach an egg

The chemical reactions in all types of cell are controlled by enzymes (B2 3 Enzymes and homeostasis, page 10).

(B2 3 Enzymes and homeostasis, page 10)

Question

3 For each cell type, explain how the structural features shown in the table above help the cell carry out its function.

Exam tip

If you are asked how a cell is specialised you must *describe* features of the cell and *explain* how they help it carry out its function.

Diffusion and osmosis

Water and dissolved substances can move in and out of cells by:

- **diffusion**
- **osmosis**.

Diffusion is the spreading of particles in a gas or in solution.

- There is a net movement from areas of higher concentration to areas of lower concentration.

- The greater the difference in concentration, the greater the rate of diffusion.

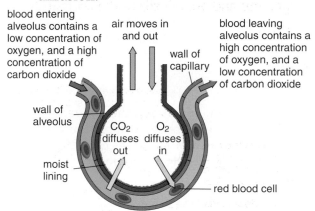

▲ Blood entering the lungs has a low oxygen concentration and a high carbon dioxide (CO_2) concentration compared to the air. So oxygen diffuses from air in the alveoli to blood and CO_2 diffuses from blood to air in the alveoli.

Osmosis is the movement of water from a dilute solution to a more concentrated solution through a partially permeable membrane.

- The concentration of water is higher in the dilute solution, because there is less dissolved material.

- Water moves through the membrane from a higher concentration of water to a lower concentration of water.

- The dissolved material cannot pass through the membrane.

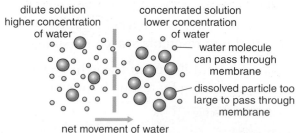

If the concentration of a solution is different inside and outside a cell, water will move in or out by osmosis.

4 Blood carrying a high concentration of oxygen flows past a cell where the oxygen concentration is low. How will oxygen move between the blood and the cell, and in which direction?

5 A plant cell and an animal cell are placed in pure water. The animal cell bursts, but the plant cell just swells. Explain why.

Exam tip

Make sure you understand the difference between these processes. Osmosis is always a movement of water and takes place through a partially permeable membrane.

Photosynthesis

Plants get the raw materials for **photosynthesis** from the air and the soil. During photosynthesis:

- chlorophyll absorbs light energy
- the energy is used to convert water and carbon dioxide into **glucose**, a type of sugar
- oxygen is released as a by-product.

The process can be summarised as:

$$\text{carbon dioxide} + \text{water} + \left(\begin{array}{c}\text{light}\\\text{energy}\end{array}\right) \rightarrow \text{glucose} + \text{oxygen}$$

Requirements of photosynthesis

Some of the sugar made during photosynthesis is used for respiration (B2 3 Enzymes and homeostasis, page 10). Excess sugar can be converted into insoluble **starch** for storage.

We can find out if a plant tissue has been photosynthesising by testing it for starch.

Exam tip

Remember: the iodine test turns starch dark blue.

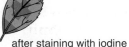

leaf attached to plant

foil stencil   after staining with iodine

▲ A foil mask is attached to a leaf for a few hours. Areas masked from the light have not produced starch.

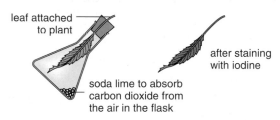

leaf attached to plant

after staining with iodine

soda lime to absorb carbon dioxide from the air in the flask

▲ A leaf is deprived of carbon dioxide for a few hours. Afterwards, it does not contain starch.

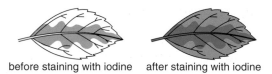

before staining with iodine   after staining with iodine

▲ Only part of this **variegated** leaf contains chlorophyll. The part without chlorophyll has not produced starch.

6 From the three experiments shown in the diagrams above, suggest **three** things required for photosynthesis.

How science works

Suggest a **control** for the second experiment above. Explain your answer.

Limiting factors

Photosynthesis is slowed down by:

- cold
- lack of light
- lack of CO_2.

Any one of these factors can slow photosynthesis even if the other factors are in plentiful supply.

For example, in a warm, bright greenhouse where there is very little CO_2, the rate of photosynthesis is limited by shortage of this gas. CO_2 is the **limiting factor**.

Even if we increase temperature or light intensity, photosynthesis does not speed up because there is not enough CO_2.

- If we increase the concentration of CO_2, photosynthesis speeds up.
- Eventually, there is so much CO_2 that it is no longer the limiting factor. Adding more CO_2 has no effect. (Point X on the graph below.)
- Now another factor is limiting. We can only increase the rate of photosynthesis by increasing that factor.

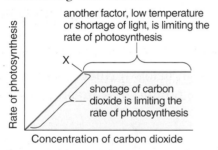

Question

7 Explain why increasing the level of CO_2 beyond point X does not speed up photosynthesis.

Exam tip

All limiting factor graphs can be interpreted like this. Only one factor is limiting at a time.

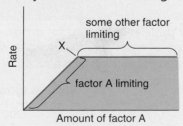

Greenhouses

In a greenhouse, we can manipulate a plant's environment using:

- heaters
- artificial lights
- CO_2 from burning fossil fuels or from gas cylinders.

We need to know which is the limiting factor in each situation. For example, if CO_2 is limiting:

- it makes sense to increase CO_2 levels
- there is no point in increasing temperature or light levels until we have supplied more CO_2.

We also need to know that too much heat, light or CO_2 is harmful.

Farmers must also look carefully at the costs of increasing these factors. If these are not covered by increased money from sales, then it becomes uneconomic to enhance the conditions.

Question

8 The rate of photosynthesis is greatest at about 27°C. A farmer warms his greenhouse from 22°C to 27°C but the crop yield does not increase. Suggest a reason for this.

Minerals needed by plants

Plants can make some of the materials they need from the glucose they produce during photosynthesis. They also need other substances, which they absorb from the soil.

A deficiency (lack) of these substances makes the plant unhealthy.

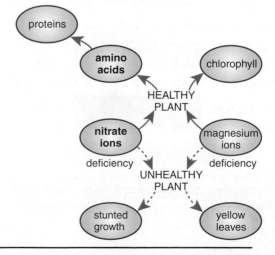

B2 2 Energy in ecosystems

- to interpret data on food chains and construct pyramids of biomass
- to explain energy flow in food chains and evaluate data on the efficiency of food
- production, including the implications of factory farming and 'food miles'
- to explain how the carbon cycle works

Food chains

The Sun is the source of energy for most communities of organisms. The only organisms that use light energy directly are green plants.

- Because they produce their own food, green plants are called **producers**.
- Organisms that eat producers are called **primary consumers**.
- Organisms that eat primary consumers are called **secondary consumers**.
- Organisms that eat secondary consumers are called **tertiary consumers**.

We can show these relationships in a food chain.

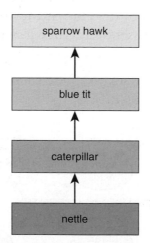

Question

1 *What is the producer in this food chain shown in the diagram above?*

Pyramids of biomass

We can measure the **biomass** (mass of living organisms) at each stage in a food chain. The biomass at each stage is less than at the previous stage. For example, a caterpillar cannot convert all the lettuce it eats into building its body. Some mass is wasted, e.g. in:

- CO_2 produced during respiration
- undigested food in faeces (droppings).

The biomass at each stage can be drawn to scale and shown as a **pyramid of biomass**. The diagram below includes **detritus**, the solid waste produced by organisms and their dead bodies.

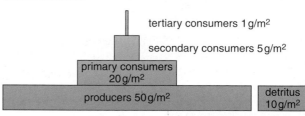

▲ We measure the biomass per unit area of habitat. The diagram shows biomass in units of grams per square metre (g/m^2).

Question

2 *Draw a pyramid of biomass for the data in the table, using an appropriate scale. What proportion of plant biomass ends up in foxes?*

Organism	Biomass (g/m^2)
plants	200
slug	70
shrew	15
fox	2

Energy flow in food chains

Green plants capture a small proportion of the energy reaching them from the Sun. It is stored as chemical energy in the plant's cells.

Each stage of the food chain contains less energy in biomass than the previous stage. This is because organisms do not use *all* the energy they take in to build biomass.

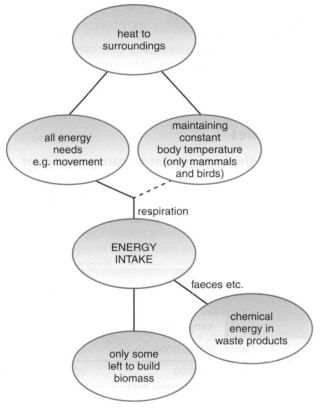

- Chemical energy is lost in waste materials.
- Respiration supplies all the organism's energy needs, including movement. A lot of the energy transformed in respiration is eventually transferred as heat to the surroundings.

Mammals and birds maintain a constant body temperature which is usually higher than that of the surroundings. This requires energy.

Exam tip

Remember: only mammals and birds maintain a constant body temperature.

Energy wastage

Each stage in the food chain wastes some energy instead of using it to make biomass.

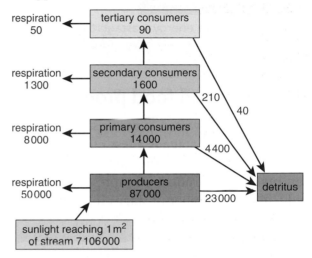

▲ Energy flow in a stream. Energy flow is measured in kJ/m^2 per year.

We can show the energy flow using a Sankey diagram. The arrows are drawn to scale. In this diagram, each square represents 0.5 kJ.

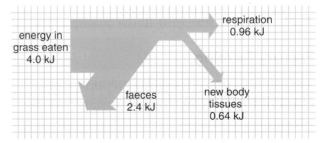

▲ Sankey diagram for a grasshopper.

Questions

3 What proportion of the energy in the grasshopper's food is converted into biomass?

4 In birds and mammals, a far lower proportion of the energy in the food is converted into biomass. Suggest a reason for this.

After revising this section, you should be able...

- to explain the function of enzymes in living things and give examples, including respiration and digestion
- to evaluate the use of enzymes in industry and in the home
- to evaluate data about the isolation of insulin and the treatment of diabetes

Enzymes

Catalysts are chemicals that increase the rate of chemical reactions.

Exam tip

Catalysts are discussed in more detail in C2 3 The tortoise or the hare, page 28.

Enzymes are the 'biological catalysts' that catalyse reactions in living organisms. They are protein molecules, made from chains of amino acids folded into a precise shape. The shape allows other molecules (**substrates**) to fit into the enzyme.

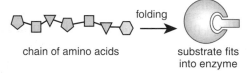

chain of amino acids   substrate fits into enzyme

The processes catalysed by enzymes inside living cells include:

- respiration
- photosynthesis
- production of amino acids, proteins and other molecules.

Question

1 Why do enzymes stop working if their shape is destroyed?

Ideal conditions for enzymes

Enzymes work best at a particular:

- temperature
- pH.

The ideal conditions differ for different enzymes.

Most enzymes in the human body work best at about 37°C. Enzymes are **denatured** by high temperatures. This means that their shape changes so that the substrate no longer fits.

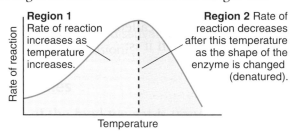

Region 1 Rate of reaction increases as temperature increases.

Region 2 Rate of reaction decreases after this temperature as the shape of the enzyme is changed (denatured).

Temperature

Exam tip

Remember: 'denature' does not mean 'kill' – it refers to a change of shape.

Question

2 Use the graph and the table below to suggest where in the body you might find enzymes A and B.

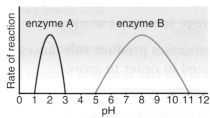

enzyme A   enzyme B

▲ Enzymes A and B work best at very different pH values.

Part of body	Typical pH
stomach	2.0
saliva	6.8
muscle	7.1
blood	7.4
small intestine	8.1

Respiration

Energy is used by:

- all organisms to build larger molecules from smaller ones (e.g. proteins from amino acids)
- animals to enable muscles to contract
- mammals and birds to maintain a steady body temperature
- plants to make amino acids from sugars, nitrates and other nutrients.

This energy is released by a series of chemical reactions called **respiration**.

Aerobic respiration is respiration that uses oxygen. Most of the reactions in aerobic respiration take place in mitochondria. The process can be summarised as:

$$\text{glucose} + \text{oxygen} \rightarrow \frac{\text{carbon}}{\text{dioxide}} + \text{water} (+ \text{energy})$$

Exam tip

Remember: plants respire all the time just as animals do. When it is light, plants also photosynthesise.

Question

3 Where do plants get the glucose that they use in respiration?

Digestion

The main types of large molecule in food are:

- carbohydrates (e.g. starch) • proteins
- lipids (fats and oils).

These molecules are too large to be absorbed into the bloodstream. **Digestion** breaks them down into small, soluble molecules.

The enzymes that catalyse digestion are produced by specialised cells in glands and in the gut lining. They pass out of the cells into the gut, where they come into contact with food.

Enzyme	Where it is produced	Function
amylase	salivary glands; pancreas; small intestine	starch → sugars in mouth and small intestine
proteases	stomach; pancreas; small intestine	proteins → amino acids in stomach and small intestine
lipases	pancreas; small intestine	fats → fatty acids and glycerol in small intestine

Type of food	Enzyme	Products
a protein molecule is made up of many different amino acids	protease	amino acids
a starch molecule is made up of many glucose molecules	amylase	glucose
a fat molecule is made up of fatty acid and glycerol molecules	lipase	fatty acids / glycerol

Question

4 Bread contains starch. Shireen notices that if she chews bread for a long time, it starts to taste sweet. Explain why.

Conditions in the gut

The stomach produces hydrochloric acid. This creates acidic conditions in which stomach enzymes work well.

The liver produces bile, which is stored in the gall bladder before being released into the small intestine. Bile neutralises stomach acid and creates alkaline conditions in which intestinal enzymes work well.

Exam tip

Bile is used in digestion but it is not an enzyme.

Enzymes in industry

Some microbes produce enzymes which pass out of the cells and can be purified.

Enzyme	Use in industry
proteases	partially digest proteins in baby foods to make them easier for babies to digest
carbohydrases (enzymes that digest carbohydrates)	convert starch into glucose syrup
isomerase	converts glucose syrup into fructose syrup

Stage 1: production of glucose syrup

starch from maize grains

↓

The enzyme amylase is added to the starch to digest it into glucose.

↓

glucose syrup

Stage 2: conversion of glucose to fructose

glucose syrup

↓

isomerase enzyme

↓

fructose syrup

Fructose syrup is used in slimming foods. It is sweeter than ordinary sugar, so less is required.

Without enzymes:

- these reactions would be extremely slow at ordinary temperatures and pressures
- expensive equipment and energy would be required.

But making the enzymes can also be expensive.

Enzymes in the home

Biological washing powders contain:

- proteases – break down proteins in stains such as blood and egg
- lipases – break down lipids in stains such as oil and grease.

Question

5 At high washing temperatures, biological powders don't work much better than ordinary ones. Why not?

Getting rid of waste

The body must remove waste products including:

- carbon dioxide – produced during respiration
- urea – produced in the liver by the breakdown of excess amino acids.

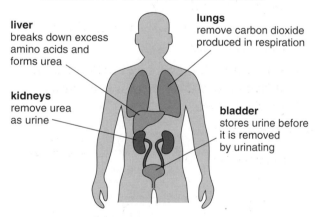

liver
breaks down excess amino acids and forms urea

lungs
remove carbon dioxide produced in respiration

kidneys
remove urea as urine

bladder
stores urine before it is removed by urinating

Exam tip

Do not confuse the 'terrible Us':
- Urea is made in the liver.
- Urine is produced in the kidney. It is stored in the bladder.

Homeostasis

The human body keeps many conditions constant, including:

- temperature (around 37°C in humans)
- water content
- ion content
- blood sugar levels.

Temperature

The **thermoregulatory** centre in the brain:

- contains receptors that sense the temperature of the blood flowing through the brain
- receives impulses from temperature receptors in the skin.

The body controls its temperature by:

- dilating (widening) and constricting (narrowing) blood vessels that supply capillaries in the skin
- producing sweat, which cools the body as it evaporates
- shivering – the energy to make muscles shiver comes from respiration, which produces heat.

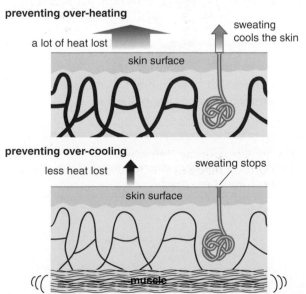

preventing over-heating

a lot of heat lost

skin surface

sweating cools the skin

preventing over-cooling

less heat lost

skin surface

sweating stops

muscle

muscle shivers

Water and ions

If the amount of water is not controlled, too much water may move into or out of cells, causing damage.

The water and ions you take in must balance the amount you lose. For example, you sweat more when it is hot, so you need to drink more.

Blood sugar

The cells in the body need a constant supply of glucose in order to respire. The glucose is carried to cells by the blood.

- Too little blood glucose means cells cannot respire properly and may be damaged.
- Too much blood glucose causes water to move out of cells by osmosis, damaging them.

The blood glucose concentration is monitored and controlled by the pancreas.

After a meal, blood glucose levels rise as carbohydrates are digested. Cells in the pancreas detect the rise in blood glucose and release a hormone called **insulin**. The bloodstream carries the insulin to all the body's cells. The hormone lets glucose move from the blood into the cells, so the level in the blood falls again.

Diabetes

In people with **diabetes**, the pancreas does not make enough insulin. People with uncontrolled diabetes may develop very high levels of glucose in the blood.

Before treatments were developed, diabetes was fatal.

Insulin

In 1922, the Canadian scientists Banting and Best managed to extract insulin from a dog pancreas. They made other dogs diabetic by removing their pancreases. These dogs were successfully treated with the insulin.

Soon, the scientists had a pure enough preparation to test on a human. They injected insulin into a diabetic child. His blood sugar level dropped.

Other scientists had tried but failed to isolate insulin from the pancreas.

Banting thought that digestive enzymes in the pancreas were destroying the insulin. So he operated on dogs to tie the pancreatic duct, the tube that allows enzymes to escape from the pancreas. A few weeks later, he took out the pancreas and extracted insulin.

How science works

Were Banting and Best justified in experimenting on animals?

Question

7 Banting also cooled the pancreas before extracting the insulin. What effect would this have on the digestive enzymes?

But later, he discovered that he could extract insulin from normal pancreas as long as he used the right methods.

How science works

Was Banting right about why others had failed to extract insulin? Explain your answer.

Treating diabetes

Many people with diabetes can live long and healthy lives. Treatments include:

- a controlled diet, to control glucose intake
- regular, controlled exercise (this increases the rate of respiration, which uses up glucose)
- regular insulin injections
- blood tests to monitor glucose levels and check that treatment is working.

You can inject insulin into the blood in several ways, including:

- ordinary injections with a needle
- through an ultra-fine needle using an 'insulin pen'
- insulin jets that fire a fine spray of insulin into the skin
- pumps that supply a continuous trickle of insulin through a needle attached to the body.

Exam tip

It is important to remember that these treatments do not *cure* diabetes.

Question

8 Why must diabetics who use insulin take care not to inject too much?

Inheriting disease

After revising this section, you should be able...

- to explain Mendel's results and why their significance was not appreciated for some time
- to interpret, analyse and construct genetic diagrams

- to make informed judgements about the social and ethical issues related to embryo research and embryo screening

Chromosomes and genes

The **chromosomes** in a cell nucleus contain a substance called **DNA** (**d**eoxyribose **n**ucleic **a**cid). The structure of DNA allows it to encode information, a bit like letters of the alphabet.

A **gene** is a small section of DNA. Each gene codes for a particular sequence of amino acids that make up a specific protein.

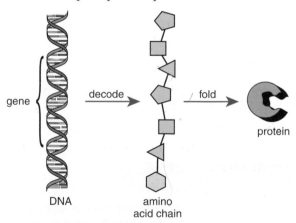

gene — DNA — decode → amino acid chain — fold → protein

Exam tip

You do not need to know details of the structure of DNA.

Question

1 Why are proteins so important for making other molecules in the cell?

We can analyse DNA to give a genetic fingerprint. Only a tiny sample is needed, e.g. a few cells from a blood stain or a hair root.

Everybody apart from identical twins has unique DNA, so the DNA fingerprint can identify an individual. This is useful in many areas, including forensic science.

Mitosis and asexual reproduction

Organisms develop from single cells by cell division. Dead cells are also replaced by cell division. This process of division is called **mitosis**. Cells produced by mitosis have identical genes to the parent cell.

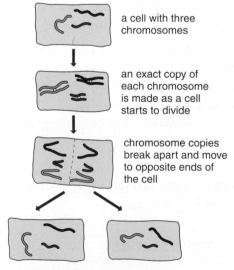

a cell with three chromosomes

an exact copy of each chromosome is made as a cell starts to divide

chromosome copies break apart and move to opposite ends of the cell

two new cells are formed, each containing exactly the same genetic information as the original cell

Some organisms reproduce by **asexual reproduction**, e.g. plants may produce runners. The cells of the offspring are produced from the parent by mitosis. The offspring is genetically identical to the parent – a **clone**.

Meiosis and sexual reproduction

In body cells the chromosomes are normally found in pairs: the cells have two sets of genetic information.

Gametes (sex cells – sperm and eggs in humans) have only one chromosome set. They are made in reproductive organs (testes and ovaries in humans) by a special type of cell division called **meiosis**.

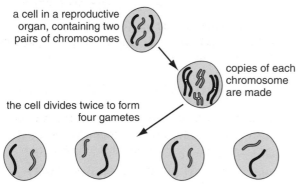

a cell in a reproductive organ, containing two pairs of chromosomes

copies of each chromosome are made

the cell divides twice to form four gametes

each gamete contains one chromosome from each pair

Gametes fuse at fertilisation, forming an ordinary cell with two chromosome sets.

This cell contains a mixture of genetic information from both parents. So unlike asexual reproduction, sexual reproduction produces genetic variation.

Questions

2 *Why can't mitosis produce gametes?*
3 *Explain why an individual formed by sexual reproduction has a different combination of alleles from either parent.*

Sex chromosomes

In humans, one pair of chromosomes (called X and Y) carry genes that determine sex.

- In female cells, the 'sex chromosomes' are the same (XX).
- In male cells, they are different (XY).

When gametes are made:

- each egg cell gets one X chromosome
- some sperm get one X, and others get one Y.

A baby's sex depends on whether the egg is fertilised by an X or a Y sperm cell.

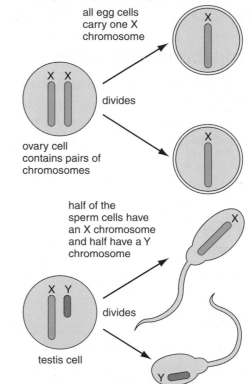

all egg cells carry one X chromosome

divides

ovary cell contains pairs of chromosomes

half of the sperm cells have an X chromosome and half have a Y chromosome

divides

testis cell

How science works

In some cultures, men could divorce their wives for not producing a male child. Most people today find this morally unacceptable.

Why is it also scientifically mistaken?

Alleles

A gene may occur in different forms called **alleles**. An example is a coat colour gene in rabbits:

- The B allele controls development of black fur.
- The b allele controls development of white fur.

Different pairs of alleles give different coat colours.

Alleles	Colour
BB	black
Bb	black
bb	white

The B allele produces black fur even when there is only one copy: Bb rabbits are black.

- We call B a **dominant** allele.

But the b allele produces white fur only when B is absent.

- We call b a **recessive** allele.

Question

4 Peas can produce smooth seeds (controlled by allele S) or wrinkled seeds (controlled by allele s). When a smooth-seeded plant is crossed with a wrinkled-seeded plant, all the offspring have smooth seeds. (a) Which allele is dominant and which is recessive? (b) What combination of alleles do these smooth-seeded offspring have?

Genetic diagrams

Genetic diagrams of crosses show:

- which alleles each parent can pass to the gametes
- which possible combinations of gametes can fertilise one another.

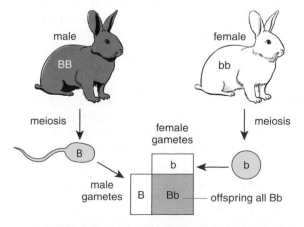

▲ Every baby rabbit must get B from one parent and b from the other. All the offspring are Bb and therefore black.

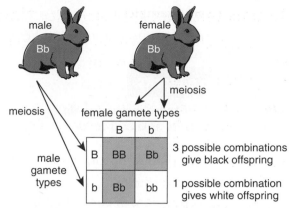

▲ Each baby rabbit can get any of four possible combinations of alleles. On average in a large sample, one rabbit in four will be white.

Exam tip

The diagram above does not mean that there are only four babies. It shows the four possible types of offspring having different allele combinations.

Always use Punnet squares rather than 'crossed lines' when drawing genetic diagrams.

Question

5 Pea plants can have red flowers, controlled by allele R, or white flowers, controlled by allele r. R is dominant. (a) What colour are Rr flowers? (b) Draw a genetic diagram for a cross between two Rr plants. (c) A scientist crosses two Rr plants. The first five offspring all have red flowers. Should the scientist be surprised? Explain your answer.

Mendel

An Austrian monk called Gregor Mendel made many discoveries about inheritance by investigating pea plants in the 1860s.

Mendel used good scientific techniques.

- He studied peas that differed in only one characteristic at a time, e.g. red/white flowers; smooth/wrinkled seeds.
- He transferred pollen between flowers using a paintbrush, so he knew exactly which parents contributed to each cross.

- He used large samples.
- He made careful observations and kept clear records.

By counting each type of offspring, Mendel concluded that:

- each characteristic was controlled by a single factor that came in different forms
- each parent had a pair of factors and passed one of them to the offspring
- the factors did not blend together in crosses, but remained intact, e.g. plants with red flowers could have white offspring: white was not lost forever or blended with red, only masked.

The importance of Mendel's work was not recognised until after his death because:

- people did not know much about chromosomes until about 1900
- they did not understand how Mendel's 'factors' were passed into gametes and offspring.

Question

6 *What would we call Mendel's 'factors' today? What about the different forms of a factor?*

Inherited diseases

Some diseases are caused by alleles that do not work normally. They can be passed from parents to children.

Cystic fibrosis is a disorder of cell membranes. People with the disease produce thick mucus in their lungs and digestive system. This causes difficulties with breathing and digestion.

The disease is caused by a recessive allele (c). A person will inherit the disease only if they have no copies of the normal allele (C).

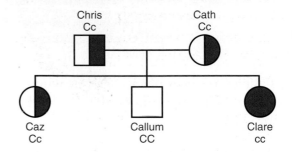

▲ Both parents carry the c allele. But they also have a C allele, so neither of them has the disease. Only Clare has the disease. Key: square – male; circle – female.

Huntington's disease is a disorder of the nervous system. People with the disease typically become ill in their 30s or 40s and eventually die.

The disease is caused by a dominant allele (H), so a person with only one copy of H will have the disease.

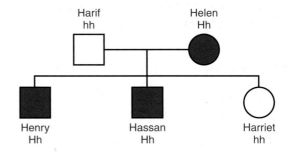

▲ Everybody with just one H allele is coloured in because they have the disease. Harriet is the only child without the disease.

Question

7 *A child is born with a genetic disease even though neither parent has the disease. Is it likely to be caused by a dominant or a recessive allele? Explain your answer.*

Genetic screening

It is possible to test embryos for these diseases and some other genetic conditions. This is **genetic screening**.

- An embryo is produced in the lab using *in vitro* fertilisation (IVF).
- When the embryo is a tiny ball of cells, a single cell can be taken without harming the embryo. The cell's DNA can be analysed.
- If the embryo has the disease, the parents may decide not to have it implanted in the mother's womb.

Some conditions can also be detected later, when the woman is already pregnant. A woman whose fetus has a serious genetic problem may be asked whether she wants an abortion.

How science works

What are the social and ethical implications of embryo testing? What about testing a fetus in a pregnant woman?

Stem cells

Most animal cells become **differentiated** at an early stage of development.

A differentiated cell is specialised to perform a particular function (B2 1 Cells and photosynthesis, page 2) and cannot develop into another type of cell.

Many plant cells are not differentiated. Even if they perform a particular function, they can develop to form other types of cell. For example, a whole plant can often be grown from a single leaf.

A small proportion of animal cells are not differentiated, so they can be made to form many different cell types. These **stem cells** are abundant in:

- early embryos
- bone marrow.

Stem cells have great potential in medicine to replace dead or damaged cells, e.g. in people paralysed by damage to neurones in the spinal cord. Differentiated neurones cannot be used, as they cannot divide to form new tissue.

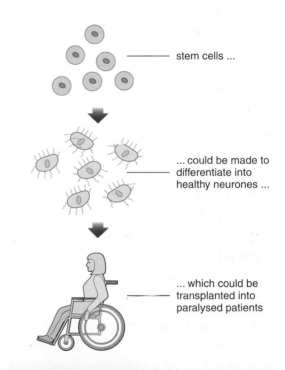

stem cells ...

... could be made to differentiate into healthy neurones ...

... which could be transplanted into paralysed patients

How science works

What are the social and ethical implications of using embryos in stem cell research?

After revising this section, you should be able...

- to represent atomic structures, and use them to explain chemical properties of atoms
- to compare properties of ionic compounds, covalent compounds, metals and macromolecules

- to suggest properties of substances given their structure and vice versa
- to evaluate applications of new materials such as nanoparticles

Atoms, elements and compounds

Remember from previous units that:

- **atoms** consist of a small central **nucleus** made of **protons** and **neutrons**, surrounded by point-like **electrons**
- there are about 100 different types of atom
- substances with only one type of atom are called **elements**
- atoms of a particular element have the same number of protons
- atoms of different elements have different numbers of protons
- in **compounds**, two or more elements are not just mixed but chemically combined.

For this unit:

- protons and electrons are electrically charged
- the number of protons in an atom is called its **proton number** or **atomic number**
- in an atom, the number of electrons equals the number of protons.

Particle	Relative charge
proton	+1 (positive)
neutron	0 (neutral)
electron	−1 (negative)

1 What is the overall electric charge on an atom? Explain your answer.

Energy levels

Electrons are arranged in zones called **energy levels** or **electron shells**.

For the first 20 elements, electrons take up simple patterns by fitting into the lowest available energy level. When one level is full, they go on to the next.

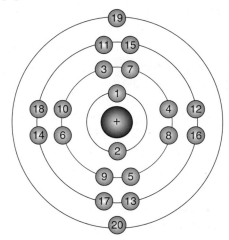

▲ This pattern applies to the first 20 elements.

Energy level	Number of electrons
1	2
2	8
3	8
4	2

For example, for the 11 electrons in a sodium (Na) atom:

- two fill the first level
- the next eight fill the second level
- the last one begins the third level.

We can represent this pattern as 2,8,1 or in a diagram.

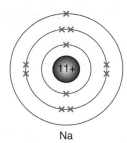

Na

Question

2 Give both representations for atoms of (a) carbon (atomic number 6), (b) phosphorus (atomic number 15), and (c) calcium (atomic number 20).

Electrons and chemistry

Only electrons in the highest energy level of an atom (outer electrons) participate in chemical reactions. Atoms with the same number of outer electrons have similar chemical properties.

Helium (2), neon (2,8) and argon (2,8,8) have a full outer energy level, giving very stable electron structures. These elements are extremely unreactive and we call them **noble gases** (Group 0).

Question

3 Copy and complete the diagram below.

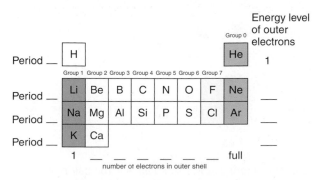

▲ Purple – alkali metals; yellow – halogens; blue – noble gases.

Ions

Atoms can transfer electrons to one another, forming charged particles called **ions**. Stable ions have the same electron structure as a noble gas. For example:

- sodium loses one electron
- fluorine gains one electron
- both ions have the same electron structure as neon.

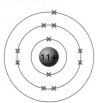

sodium atom

sodium ion

neon atom

Questions

4 Copy and complete the table below.

Element	Atom symbol	Atom electron structure	Ion symbol	Ion electron structure
sodium	Na	2,8,1	Na+	[2,8]+
potassium	K			
magnesium	Mg	2,8,2	Mg^{2+}	$[2,8]^{2+}$
calcium	Ca			
oxygen	O		O^{2-}	
fluorine	F	2,7	F⁻	[2,8]–
chlorine	Cl			

5 Look at the diagram of Na+ and draw similar diagrams of (a) F⁻, and (b) O^{2-}.

Ionic compounds

- Metals tend to lose electrons.
- Non-metals tend to gain electrons.
- They react together to form **ionic compounds**.

For example:

- Group 1 elements – alkali metals – react with Group 7 elements – **halogens**
- they form ionic compounds containing metal ions with a single positive charge and **halide** ions with a single negative charge.

Ionic compounds form giant 3D **lattices** held together by the electrostatic attraction between negative and positive charges. This method of joining is called an **ionic bond**.

Property of ionic compounds	Explanation
high melting and boiling points	strong attraction in all directions between positive and negative ions
conduct electricity, but only when molten or dissolved	ions can move around

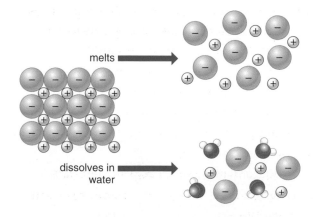

melts ➡

dissolves in water ➡

6 Why can't ionic compounds conduct electricity when they are solid?

Metals

Atoms in metals are arranged in a regular lattice. The outer electrons are delocalised, i.e. they are free to move throughout the structure.

So metals contain positive ions and delocalised electrons, held together by electrostatic attraction.

Property of metals	Explanation
can be bent and shaped	layers of atoms can slide over each other
good conductors of heat and electricity	delocalised electrons can move around

Covalent compounds

Non-metals need to gain electrons to get a stable electron structure. They can react together by sharing electrons to form **molecules** – groups of atoms linked by **covalent bonds**. We can represent molecules in several ways.

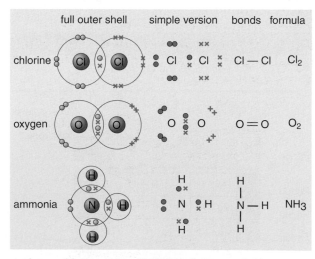

	full outer shell	simple version	bonds	formula
chlorine			Cl — Cl	Cl_2
oxygen			O = O	O_2
ammonia				NH_3

▲ a) two chlorine atoms share an electron pair b) two oxygen atoms share two electron pairs and are joined by two covalent bonds c) a nitrogen atom shares electron pairs with three hydrogen atoms.

Property of covalent compounds	Explanation
relatively low melting and boiling points	only weak forces *between* molecules (**intermolecular forces**) must be broken for melting and boiling. Strong covalent bonds holding each molecule together remain intact
do not conduct electricity	molecules have no overall charge

Giant covalent structures

Some atoms that share electrons can form giant covalent structures or **macromolecules** containing very many atoms, e.g. carbon atoms can form diamond or graphite.

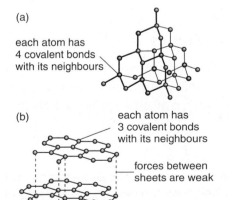

(a)

each atom has 4 covalent bonds with its neighbours

(b)

each atom has 3 covalent bonds with its neighbours

forces between sheets are weak

▲ a) diamond, b) graphite.

- The giant structures give macromolecules very high melting and boiling points.
- The lattice structure of diamond makes it extremely hard.
- The sheets in graphite can slide over each other, making it soft and slippery.
- Each atom in graphite has an unshared electron. These electrons can move around, so graphite conducts heat and electricity, a bit like a metal.

Nanomaterials

Materials change their **properties** when they are cut up small enough.

Nanoparticles are particles between 1 and 100 nanometres across. These particles contain only a few hundred atoms or so. Possible uses in the future include:

- catalysts – a very fine powder has a very large surface area where chemical reactions can take place
- computers using the special properties of nanoparticles
- light, strong construction materials
- waterproof, fireproof or stain resistant coatings.

After revising this section, you should be able...

- to calculate chemical quantities involving formula mass and percentage of elements in compounds
- to calculate reacting masses and percentage yields
- to evaluate industrial processes in terms of atom economy and sustainable development

Isotopes

Atoms of a particular element always have the same number of protons. But they may have different numbers of neutrons.

Atoms of the same element with different numbers of neutrons are called **isotopes**.

We can describe an atom by giving its:

- atomic number (number of protons)
- **mass number** (= total number of protons + neutrons).

$$\text{mass number} \longrightarrow \ \ 12$$
$$\mathbf{C}$$
$$\text{atomic number} \longrightarrow \ \ 6$$

▲ Carbon-12 has 6 protons and 6 neutrons.

Question

1 (a) $^{14}_{6}C$ is another isotope of carbon. How many protons and neutrons does it have?
(b) Chlorine's atomic number is 17. The most common isotope has 18 neutrons. Write a symbol for this atom.

Relative atomic mass

- Protons and neutrons have almost identical masses.
- Electrons have a much smaller mass.

The mass of an atom is so small that it is inconvenient to give it in grams. It's simpler just to call the mass of a proton or a neutron '1 unit'.

Particle	Relative mass
proton	1
neutron	1
electron	tiny

In practice, instead of calling the proton mass 1 unit, we call the mass of a $^{12}_{6}C$ nucleus 12 units. We say that carbon has a **relative atomic mass (A_r)** of 12.

The masses of other atoms are measured relative to carbon. For example, A_r for sodium is 23: a sodium atom has almost twice the mass of a carbon atom.

Question

2 The A_r of helium is 4 and of silver is 108. (a) How many helium atoms have the same mass as one carbon atom? (b) How many carbon atoms have the same mass as one silver atom?

A_r and isotopes

Atoms of different isotopes have different masses. The A_r of an element is an average of the relative atomic masses of all its isotopes.

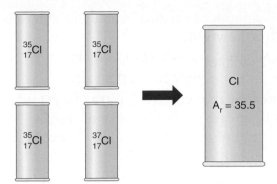

▲ The two common isotopes of chlorine have mass numbers 35 and 37. $^{35}_{17}Cl$ is more common than $^{37}_{17}Cl$, and the average A_r is 35.5.

Relative formula mass

Just as each element has a relative atomic mass, so each compound has a relative **formula mass (M_r)**.

To find M_r, add the relative atomic masses of all the atoms in the compound.

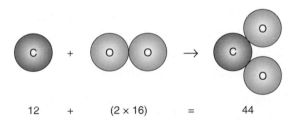

$$12 \quad + \quad (2 \times 16) \quad = \quad 44$$

▲ Relative formula mass of carbon dioxide.

We can use A_r and M_r to calculate the percentage of a particular atom in a compound. For example:

- M_r for carbon dioxide = 44
- amount of oxygen = $2 \times 16 = 32$
- percentage of oxygen = $\dfrac{32}{44} \times 100 = 72.7\%$

3 Use the data in the following table to find relative formula masses for (a) ammonia (NH_3), and (b) iron oxide (Fe_2O_3).

Element	hydrogen	nitrogen	oxygen	iron
A_r	1	14	16	55.8

4 What percentage of ammonia is nitrogen?

The mole

12 g of carbon contain about 6×10^{23} (600 000 000 000 000 000 000 000) atoms. This huge number is called a **mole**. If you take A_r of an element (or M_r of a compound) in grams, you always have a mole of particles, e.g.

- 23 g of sodium is 1 mole of Na atoms
- 44 g of carbon dioxide is 1 mole of CO_2 molecules.

Reactions and masses

We can work out the masses of reactants and products by:

- writing a balanced equation
- using A_r and M_r to calculate masses.

For example:

How much carbon do we need to reduce 160 g of CuO, and what mass of products do we get?

Element	A_r
copper	64
carbon	12
oxygen	16

$$2CuO \quad + C \rightarrow 2Cu + \quad CO_2$$
$$2 \times (64 + 16) : 12 \rightarrow 2 \times 64 : (12 + 2 \times 16)$$
$$160 \quad : 12 \rightarrow 128 : \quad 44$$

So 160 g of copper oxide reacts with 12 g of carbon to produce 128 g of copper and 44 g of CO_2.

Calculate the total mass of reactants and the total mass of products. Explain the result.

Question

5 When limestone is heated, $CaCO_3 \rightarrow CaO + CO_2$. A_r for calcium is 40. What mass of each product is formed when 50 g of limestone is heated?

Atom economy

The amount of useful product you get as a percentage of the total products is called the **atom economy** of a reaction.

For example, extracting copper from CuO using carbon gives 128 g copper out of a total of 172 g, so

$$\text{atom economy} = \frac{128}{172} \times 100 = 74.4\%.$$

Often there is a choice of reactions to produce the same product. For economic reasons and for **sustainable development**, it is important to choose one with good atom economy.

Question

6 Another way we can produce copper is via the reaction $CuS + O_2 \rightarrow Cu + SO_2$. A_r for sulfur is 32. Which method has greater atom economy?

Yield

In real life, we do not always get as much product as we expect, because:

- the reaction may not go to completion
- other reactions may take place as well as the expected one
- it may be hard to separate the product from the reaction mix.

The amount of product actually produced is called the **yield**.

For example:

Imagine that you react 160 g of CuO with 12 g of carbon, and get 96 g of copper instead of the expected 128 g. Then

yield = 96 g

$$\textbf{percentage yield} = \frac{96}{128} \times 100 = 75\%.$$

Question

7 Nic heats 100 g of $CaCO_3$ and gets 50.4 g CaO. What is the percentage yield?

Reversible reactions

Some chemical reactions can go in either direction. For example:

- heating ammonium chloride gives ammonia and hydrogen chloride
- cooling ammonia and hydrogen chloride gives ammonium chloride.

$$\text{ammonium chloride} \rightleftharpoons \text{ammonia} + \text{hydrogen chloride}$$

Equilibrium

The reaction of iron with steam is another reversible reaction.

$$\text{iron} + \text{steam} \rightleftharpoons \text{iron oxide} + \text{hydrogen}$$

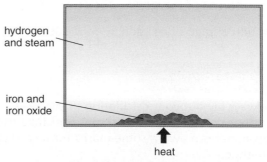

hydrogen and steam

iron and iron oxide

heat

all four substances exist in a closed system

Imagine carrying out this reaction in a **closed system** (where nothing is added or removed – e.g. a sealed box). The box will contain all four substances.

- The forward reaction uses up iron and steam, and makes iron oxide and hydrogen.
- The back reaction uses up iron oxide and hydrogen, and makes iron and steam.
- When the two reactions are going at exactly the same rate, the amounts of each chemical stay the same.
- This is called **equilibrium**.

Exam tip

At equilibrium, the forward and back reactions do not stop. They occur at the same rate so they simply balance one another out.

The Haber process

Ammonia is used for making fertiliser and explosives. It can be produced by the reaction:

nitrogen + hydrogen $\rightleftharpoons$ ammonia
$$N_2 + 3H_2 \rightleftharpoons 2NH_3$$

Nitrogen is obtained from the air. Hydrogen may be obtained from natural gas or other sources.

The forward reaction makes ammonia, but the back reaction breaks it down again. There is so little ammonia at equilibrium that the reaction is not economical.

But equilibrium is only reached in a closed system. If you open the 'sealed box' and take out the ammonia, the back reaction cannot happen.

In the **Haber process**, the ammonia is removed by cooling the gas mixture so that the ammonia condenses.

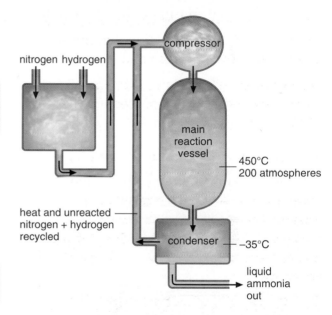

After revising this section, you should be able...

- to use data and graphs to calculate reaction rates
- to explain and evaluate methods of increasing reaction rates
- to evaluate the uses of catalysts in industrial processes

Rates of reaction

The rate of a chemical reaction depends on the conditions. For example, the reaction

glucose + oxygen → carbon dioxide + water

happens slowly in respiration, but quickly if you set fire to the glucose and burn it.

$$\textbf{rate of reaction} = \frac{\text{amount of reactant used}}{\text{time}} \text{ or } \frac{\text{amount of product produced}}{\text{time}}$$

For example:

A scientist adds sodium carbonate to hydrochloric acid and measures the volume of carbon dioxide produced:

$$Na_2CO_3 + 2HCl \rightarrow 2NaCl + H_2O + CO_2$$

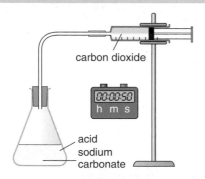

carbon dioxide

`00:00:50`
h m s

acid
sodium
carbonate

Question

1 Draw a graph of the figures in the table below and use it to calculate the reaction rate. (Take account of any anomalous data, and give appropriate units for the rate.)

Time (s)		20	40	60	80	100
Volume of CO_2 (cm³)		12	18	29	31	51

Exam tip

Remember: calculating a rate from a graph is the same as calculating a gradient. As a reaction proceeds, its rate generally goes down because the reactants get used up.

Colliding atoms

Particles can only react when they meet. When they react, chemical bonds must be broken, which requires energy. So reactions can only occur when particles:

- collide with each other
- collide with enough energy.

The minimum energy the particles need in order to react is called the **activation energy** for that particular reaction.

Changing reaction rates

The simplest ways to speed up a reaction are by:

- making collisions more likely
- making collisions more energetic.

Exam tip

All the following methods change reaction *rate*. Do not confuse this with *yield*.

Temperature

The higher the temperature, the more energy the particles have. So

- increasing temperature increases reaction rate.

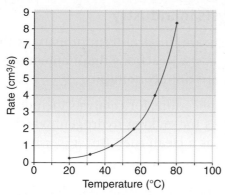

▲ Varying the temperature of the sodium carbonate/hydrochloric acid reaction.

Concentration

Concentration measures the number of particles in a given volume. It is measured in moles per cubic decimetre (mol/dm^3).

- Equal volumes of solutions with equal concentrations contain the same number of moles of dissolved material.
- Equal volumes of gases at the same temperature and pressure contain the same number of moles.
- The higher the pressure, the more moles of gas are squeezed into $1\,dm^3$.

The more crowded the particles are, the more likely they are to collide. So:

- in a solution, increasing concentration increases reaction rate
- in a gas, increasing pressure increases reaction rate.

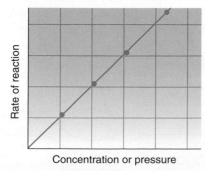

▲ Reaction rate increases with concentration or pressure.

Exam tip

Draw a revision diagram showing particles of water and acid in dilute and concentrated solutions of acid.

Draw another diagram showing particles of a gas under low and high pressure.

Question

2 The concentration of CO_2 in the atmosphere is increasing. What effect would you expect this to have on the rate of photosynthesis? Explain your answer.

Surface area

Only the particles on the surface of a solid can collide with other particles and react. So:

- increasing surface area increases reaction rate.

Breaking the solid into smaller pieces increases surface area and exposes more particles on the surface.

Question

3 Coal is safe enough to burn in domestic fires. But coal dust in mines can cause explosions. Explain why.

Catalysts

The other way to speed up a reaction is to lower its activation energy. **Catalysts** are chemicals that do this.

Catalysts:

- speed up the reaction
- are regenerated at the end of the reaction, i.e. they are not used up.

Exam tip

Catalysts do not give the particles more energy – they just enable particles with less energy to react.

Different reactions need different catalysts, e.g.

Catalyst	Reaction
manganese dioxide (MnO_2)	hydrogen peroxide $\rightarrow$ oxygen and water
iron	hydrogen + nitrogen $\rightarrow$ ammonia (Haber process)
nickel	hydrogenation of unsaturated oils, e.g. for chocolate, margarine
enzymes in yeast	sugar $\rightarrow$ alcohol (brewing)
other enzymes	various uses (B2 3 Enzymes and homeostasis, page 10)

Question

4 A scientist adds 1 g MnO_2 to hydrogen peroxide and waits for the reaction to stop, then filters the product and dries the MnO_2. How much would you expect there to be? Do you think the scientist would get this amount in real life? Explain your answers.

A simple model of how catalysts work is that bonds in the reactants are weakened on the surface of the catalyst. So increasing the catalyst's surface area increases its effect.

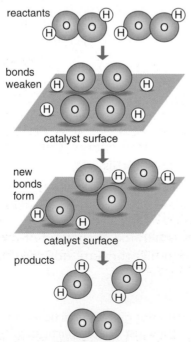

▲ Hydrogen peroxide breaks down into water and oxygen on the surface of a catalyst.

Catalysts in industry

Catalysts are important in industry as they reduce costs. Reactions that happen too slowly are not economical.

New applications for catalysts include processes for making hydrogen, which can be burned as a clean fuel. But it is usually made:

- from fossil fuels, or
- from water, using electricity that is usually generated by burning fossil fuels.

These methods release pollution.

Scientists are working on other ways of making hydrogen from water, using less polluting reactions. These reactions use catalysts to speed them up.

Catalysts are also important in reducing exhaust pollution. Car fumes contain toxic gases. The gases can react to produce less harmful products.

The catalytic converter in a car speeds up these reactions.

How science works

Heating reactions speeds them up, but it also costs money. Suggest another disadvantage of heating some reactions, especially in the food industry.

Exam tip

Copy the concept map below and add the following: temperature, surface area, pressure, catalyst, energy of collisions.

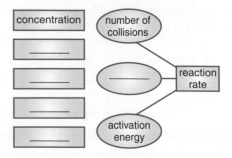

The energy bank

- to explain the effects on a reaction of changing reaction conditions
- to evaluate the choice of conditions for industrial processes in terms of chemical yield and energy requirements

Reactions and energy transfer

Chemical reactions transfer energy to or from the surroundings.

Exothermic reactions

Reactions that transfer energy to the surroundings are called **exothermic** reactions. Examples include:

- **combustion** (burning) reactions, e.g.
  $CH_4 + 2O_2 \rightarrow CO_2 + 2H_2O$
- neutralisation reactions (where an acid reacts with an alkali), e.g.
  $HCl + KOH \rightarrow KCl + H_2O$
- many oxidation reactions (reactions with oxygen), e.g.
  $2Zn + O_2 \rightarrow 2ZnO$.

As an exothermic reaction releases energy, it warms up. This is most obvious for rapid reactions like combustion.

COOLER   HOTTER

A + B → C + D + energy

chemical energy

1. Write word equations for each of the above three examples of exothermic reactions.
2. Write a balanced symbol equation for the combustion of carbon.

When we burn fuel, we have to light it. Doesn't that mean that we are transferring energy into the reaction?

The answer is that we do need to supply a little energy to kick-start the reaction – this is the activation energy that lets the first few particles react. But once the reaction is going, it continues by itself and releases a lot of energy.

Endothermic reactions

Reactions that transfer energy from the surroundings are called **endothermic** reactions. Examples include:

- thermal decomposition reactions, e.g.
  $CaCO_3 \xrightarrow{\text{heat}} CaO + CO_2$

We have to supply energy to make these reactions go. As the reaction transforms this energy into chemical energy, it cools down.

HOTTER   COOLER

A + B + energy → C + D

chemical energy

3. Write a balanced symbol equation for the thermal decomposition of zinc carbonate.

How science works

Are the following biological reactions exothermic or endothermic?
- The reaction of bile with stomach acid.
- Respiration.
- Photosynthesis.

Explain your answers.

Exam tip

Energy *exits* from exothermic reactions and *enters* endothermic reactions.

Energy transfer and reversible reactions

In blue copper sulfate crystals, water molecules are chemically bound into the crystal structure.

- We call substances that are bound to water 'hydrated'.

If you heat the crystals, water is driven off to leave a white powder of pure copper sulfate.

- We call substances without bound water 'anhydrous'.

hydrated   anhydrous
   copper $\rightleftharpoons$ copper   + water
sulfate (blue)   sulfate (white)

We need to supply energy to hydrated copper sulfate to drive off the water.

- The forward reaction is endothermic.

If you add water to anhydrous copper sulfate to regenerate hydrated copper sulfate, the reaction warms up.

- The back reaction is exothermic.

If a reversible reaction is exothermic in one direction, it will be endothermic in the other. Exactly the same amount of energy is transferred in each case.

Question

4 *Explain why a reversible reaction can not be exothermic in both directions, or endothermic in both directions.*

How science works

Suggest how anhydrous copper sulfate could be used as a chemical test for water.

Temperature and equilibrium

Remember that a reversible reaction in a closed system will reach equilibrium when the forward reaction and the back reaction are happening at the same rate.

Imagine a closed system containing hydrated copper sulfate, anhydrous copper sulfate and water.

- Supplying thermal energy (heating) drives the endothermic reaction, i.e. produces more anhydrous copper sulfate and water.
- Removing thermal energy (cooling) drives the exothermic reaction, i.e. produces more hydrated copper sulfate.

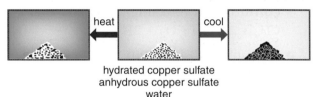

hydrated copper sulfate
anhydrous copper sulfate
water

So we can change the relative amounts of the substances at equilibrium by changing the temperature.

Raising temperature	Lowering temperature
increases yield from endothermic reaction	increases yield from exothermic reaction
decreases yield from exothermic reaction	decreases yield from endothermic reaction

Pressure and equilibrium

In gaseous reversible reactions, we can change the balance of the reacting substances at equilibrium by changing the pressure. For example:

$$N_2 + 3H_2 \rightleftharpoons 2NH_3$$

The forward reaction halves the number of molecules, which halves the volume of gas.

Imagine a closed system containing nitrogen, hydrogen and ammonia.

- Increasing pressure pushes the molecules closer together. The reaction decreases in volume by decreasing the number of molecules (making more ammonia).

- Decreasing the pressure allows the molecules to spread apart. The reaction increases in volume by increasing the number of molecules (making more nitrogen and hydrogen).

So we can change the relative amounts of the substances at equilibrium by changing the pressure.

- Increasing the pressure increases the yield for the reaction that produces fewer molecules.

Condition	Rate	Yield from exothermic reaction	Yield from endothermic reaction
high temperature			
low temperature			

Condition	Rate	Yield from reaction making more molecules	Yield from reaction making fewer molecules
high pressure			
low pressure			

These factors must be balanced against the cost of creating a high temperature or low pressure. Conditions close to atmospheric temperature and pressure mean less cost, and less energy used and released into the environment.

Conditions in the Haber process

The forward reaction in the Haber process (the production of ammonia):

- is exothermic
- decreases the number of molecules.

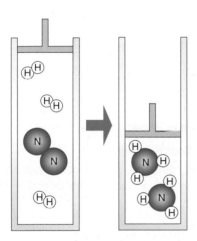

Questions

5 Copy and complete the following table.

Condition	Rate	Ammonia yield	Cost
low temperature			
high temperature			
low pressure			
high pressure			

6 The reaction is actually run at about 450°C and 200 atmospheres. Explain how this compromises between rate, yield and cost.

- to complete and balance electrode half equations
- to predict the results of electrolysing solutions
- to suggest methods for making given soluble or insoluble salts

Electrolysis

When a voltage is applied across an ionic substance that is molten or in solution:

- positively charged ions are attracted to the negative electrode
- negatively charged ions are attracted to the positive electrode.

The substance is broken down into elements. This is called **electrolysis**.

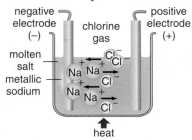

▲ Electrolysis of molten sodium chloride.

Oxidation and reduction

At the negative electrode, sodium ions combine with electrons (e^-) to give sodium atoms.

$$Na^+ + e^- \rightarrow Na$$

At the positive electrode, chloride ions give up their extra electron, leaving chlorine atoms. The atoms pair covalently, giving chlorine molecules.

$$2Cl^- \rightarrow Cl_2 + 2e^-$$

Exam tip

Both the atoms and the electric charges must be balanced.

Each **half equation** shows what happens at one of the electrodes. These two half reactions are called:

- **reduction** (gain of electrons)
- **oxidation** (loss of electrons).

Exam tip

Remember: *OilRig* – Oxidation *is loss* of electrons; Reduction *is gain* of electrons.

Question

1 *Magnesium is extracted by electrolysing molten magnesium chloride ($MgCl_2$). (a) Write a balanced half equation for each electrode. (b) Which ion is oxidised and which is reduced?*

Electrolysing solutions

When sodium chloride is dissolved in water, there is a mixture of ions:

- Na^+ and Cl^-
- H^+ and OH^- from the water.

How science works

Water is covalent. But a small proportion always breaks down into H^+ and OH^- ions.

How do we know which element will be released at each electrode?

- For positive ions, the ion of the *less reactive* element is discharged.
- For negative ions, *halide* ions are generally discharged, not hydroxide.

Release of hydrogen and chlorine leaves behind Na^+ and OH^-, i.e. a solution of sodium hydroxide.

very reactive

potassium
sodium
calcium
magnesium
aluminium
carbon
zinc
iron
tin
lead
hydrogen
copper
silver
gold
platinum

unreactive

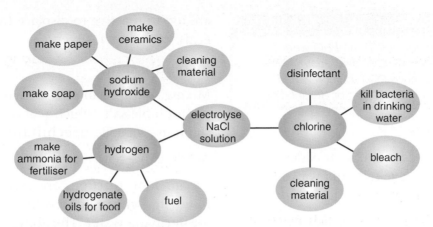

All three products are important in industry.

Question

2 Use the rules and the reactivity series to explain which elements we get from electrolysing sodium chloride solution.

Purifying copper

Impure copper extracted from ore is purified by electrolysing copper sulfate solution using copper electrodes.

- Dissolved copper ions are attracted to the negative electrode, where they gain electrons to form pure metallic copper.

- Copper from the positive electrode loses electrons to form copper ions, which dissolve.

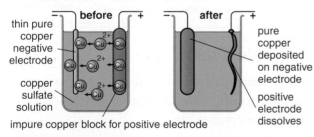

impure copper block for positive electrode

Acids and alkalis

Acids contain hydrogen.

- In solution, it is in the form of H^+ ions.

- The greater the concentration of H^+, the more acidic the solution. Soluble hydroxides are called alkalis.

- Solutions of alkalis contain OH^- ions.

The greater the concentration of OH^-, the more alkaline the solution.

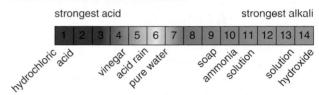

▲ The acidity or alkalinity of a solution is measured on the **pH scale**. **Universal indicator** changes colour depending on pH.

Salts

Acids and alkalis react together in **neutralisation** reactions. For example:

$$KOH\ (aq) + HCl\ (aq) \rightarrow KCl\ (aq) + H_2O\ (l)$$

Notice the **state symbols** in brackets:

- (aq) – dissolved in water
- (l) – liquid.

The other state symbols are:

- (s) – solid
- (g) – gas.

In a neutralisation:

- H^+ and OH^- react to form water

- the metal ion from the alkali and the negative ion from the acid form a compound called a **salt** – common table salt (sodium chloride) is just one member of this family of compounds.

The products are neither acidic nor alkaline. Universal indicator will show when the reactants have fully reacted.

Question

3 You have solutions of KOH and HCl with equal concentrations. Use ideas about moles to explain how much KOH solution would react completely with 10 cm³ of HCl solution.

Salts from bases

Insoluble metal oxides and hydroxides also react with acids to give salts and water. For example:

$$CuO \ (s) + H_2SO_4 \ (aq) \rightarrow CuSO_4 \ (aq) + H_2O \ (l)$$

A compound which reacts with acids is called a **base**. (Alkalis are a type of base.)

How science works

How does the method shown in the diagram below make sure that all the acid gets used up?

1 Add copper oxide (or hydroxide) to sulfuric acid and stir until it has all dissolved.

sulfuric acid
copper oxide

2 Add more copper oxide a little at a time until no more will react and dissolve.

copper sulfate solution
undissolved copper oxide

3 Filter out the unused copper oxide. The clear filtrate will be copper sulfate solution.

copper sulfate solution

4 Let the water evaporate away to give blue copper sulfate crystals.

copper sulfate crystals

▲ A solid salt can be crystallised from its solution.

Salts from metals

Metals react with acids to give salts and hydrogen. For example:

$$Mg \ + \ 2HNO_3 \ \rightarrow \ Mg(NO_3)_2 \ + H_2$$

Question

4 Copy the equation above and add state symbols.

Some metals are too reactive for this to be done safely, e.g. sodium, potassium. Others are too unreactive to displace hydrogen from acids, e.g. copper, silver.

Insoluble salts

Mixing solutions of ions sometimes generates an insoluble salt, which will come out of the solution as a solid **precipitate**. For example:

$$AgNO_3 \ (aq) + NaCl \ (aq) \rightarrow AgCl \ (s) + NaNO_3 \ (aq)$$

Precipitation reactions are useful for removing unwanted ions from solutions, e.g. for purifying water. The above reaction will remove toxic silver ions.

How science works

How would you make a pure sample of silver chloride?

Question

5 Which pairs of compounds in the diagram below would you react to give (a) sodium nitrate (b) calcium chloride (c) magnesium sulfate (d) lead iodide (insoluble)?

nitric acid

lead nitrate solution

sodium hydroxide solution

magnesium oxide

sulfuric acid

hydrochloric acid

calcium hydroxide solution

magnesium iodide solution

sodium chloride

lead oxide

Ammonium salts

Ammonia dissolves in water to give an alkaline solution. It acts rather like a solution of a metal hydroxide.

Ammonia solution is used to produce ammonium salts, which are used as fertilisers.

Exam tip

Remember: the salt takes the name of the acid. Hydro*chloric* acid produces *chlorides*; *sulf*uric acid produces *sulfates*; *nitr*ic acid produces *nitrates*.

Forces and motion

After revising this section, you should be able...

- to construct distance–time graphs and velocity–time graphs, and use them to calculate speeds, accelerations and distances
- to suggest and explain which forces act on an object, and calculate their resultant and the acceleration it causes
- to explain in terms of forces how bodies reach terminal velocity, and to draw and interpret graphs showing this

Distance–time graphs

A **distance–time graph** shows:

- the time taken since the start of a journey on the *x*-axis
- the distance travelled since the start of a journey on the *y*-axis.

For example:

> Jim leaves his house and walks 400 m to Kate's house in 300 s. He waits 200 s for Kate. Now they are late for school, so they run the last 300 m in 50 s.

Total time (s)	Total distance (m)
0	0
300	400
500	400
550	700

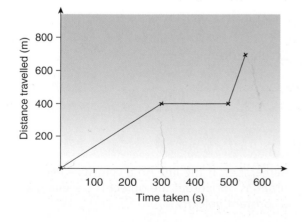

Calculating speed

- The first part of the graph slopes upwards a bit – Jim is walking.
- The second part is horizontal – Jim is stationary.
- The third part slopes upwards steeply – Jim is running. The faster Jim's **speed**, the greater the slope.

> speed = slope of distance–time graph

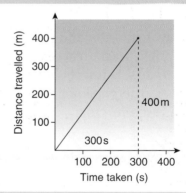

For the first section:

$$\text{speed} = \frac{400\,\text{m}}{300\,\text{s}} = 1.33\,\text{m/s}$$

Exam tip

Remember: if the line on a distance–time graph is horizontal, the object is stationary.

Question

1 Use the graph to calculate Jim's speed for the other two parts of the journey.

Velocity

Velocity means speed in a given direction.

- If speed changes, velocity changes.
- If direction changes, velocity changes (even if speed is constant).

For example:

- a car getting faster or slower changes velocity – speed is changing
- a car going round a roundabout at constant speed changes velocity – direction is changing.

Velocity–time graphs

A **velocity–time graph** shows:

- the time taken since the start of a journey on the *x*-axis
- the velocity on the *y*-axis.

For example:

A tram leaves the stop and speeds up along a straight track, reaching a velocity of 12 m/s in 20 s. It travels at 12 m/s for another 20 s. Then it slows down steadily, coming to rest after 30 s.

Total time (s)	Velocity (m/s)
0	0
20	12
40	12
70	0

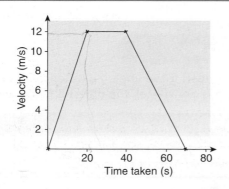

Calculating acceleration

The rate at which velocity changes is called **acceleration**. If velocity is constant, acceleration is zero.

- An object that is stationary, or moving at a constant speed in a straight line, has zero acceleration.
- An object whose speed or direction is changing is accelerating.

$$\text{acceleration} \ (\text{m/s}^2) = \frac{\text{change in velocity (m/s)}}{\text{time taken for change (s)}}$$

Exam tip

Always remember equations with their units. Units matter!

- The first part of the graph in this example slopes upwards – the tram is getting faster at a constant rate.
- The second part is horizontal – the tram's velocity is constant.
- The third part slopes downwards – the tram is getting slower at a constant rate.

acceleration = slope of velocity–time graph

If an object is slowing down, acceleration and the slope of the velocity–time graph are negative.

For the first section:

$$\text{Acceleration} = \frac{12 \,\text{m/s}}{20 \,\text{s}}$$

$$= 0.6 \,\text{m/s}^2$$

Exam tip

Remember: if the line on a velocity–time graph is horizontal the object is travelling at a constant velocity.

2 *Use the graph to calculate the tram's acceleration for the other two parts of the journey.*

Calculating distance

$$\frac{\text{distance travelled}} {} = \text{area under velocity–time graph}$$

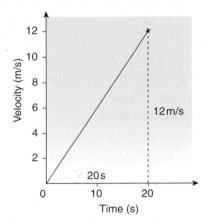

You may have to split the graph into sections to work out the area.

For the first section:

distance travelled $= \frac{1}{2} \times 20\,\text{s} \times 12\,\text{m/s} = 120\,\text{m}$

Exam tip

Remember:
area of a rectangle = base × height
area of a triangle = ½ × base × height

Question

3 *Use the graph to calculate how far the tram travelled during the other two parts of the journey.*

Weight

When you are on Earth, gravity pulls down on you. This force is called your **weight**.

Weight depends on:

- how much 'stuff' (mass) the object contains, e.g. gravity pulls with a greater force on an elephant than on a mouse
- where the object is, e.g. the Moon's gravity is weaker than the Earth's: the Moon has a smaller **gravitational field strength**. If you stood on the Moon, your weight would be less than on Earth.

$$\begin{array}{ccc} \text{weight} & & \text{gravitational} \\ \text{(newton, N)} & = \text{mass (kg)} \times & \text{field strength} \\ & & \text{(N/kg)} \end{array}$$

Questions

4 *The gravitational field strength on Earth is 10 N/kg. What is the weight of a 40 kg child?*
5 *The same child has a weight of 64 N on the Moon. What is the gravitational field strength there?*

Exam tip

Imagine someone is confused about the difference between mass and weight. How would you explain it to them?

Resultant force

If two or more forces act on the same object, we can replace them with a single force that has the same effect as the original forces all acting together.

It is called the **resultant force**.

20 N → ← 20 N
balanced forces
resultant = 0

30 N → ← 20 N
resultant = 10 N to right

Question

6 *A stone with a weight of 8 N is lifted with an upward force of 20 N. Draw a force diagram and calculate the size and direction of the resultant force.*

Interacting objects

Whenever two objects interact, the forces they exert on one another are:

- the same size
- in opposite directions.

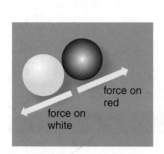

pull of Earth on person = weight

force on red

force on white

pull of person on Earth

Force and acceleration

Force causes acceleration. If there is no resultant force on an object, it will not accelerate.

- If it is stationary, it will remain stationary.
- If it is moving, it will continue at the same speed in the same direction.

If the resultant force on an object is not zero, the object will accelerate in the direction of the force.

$$\text{resultant force (N)} = \text{mass (kg)} \times \text{acceleration (m/s}^2)$$

Questions

7 What resultant force is required to make an object with mass 15 kg accelerate at 3 m/s²?

8 An object with mass 4 kg experiences a resultant downward force of 20 N. What is its acceleration?

How science works

Which of the following quantities have a direction?

- distance
- mass
- speed
- force
- velocity
- acceleration.

Stopping distance

The brakes on a car exert a force that causes the car to slow down. For example, when you see a STOP sign:

- you take a short time to react before putting on the brakes – the distance the car goes in this time is called the **thinking distance**
- you apply the brakes and the car slows down – the distance the car goes from this point before stopping is called the **braking distance**.

The total **stopping distance** from when you see the sign till the car stops is given by:

$$\text{stopping distance} = \text{thinking distance} + \text{braking distance}$$

Braking distance depends on the car's speed:

- For a given braking force, the faster the car is going, the further it will travel before stopping, or
- the faster the car is going, the more braking force you must apply to stop it in a given distance.

Stopping distance also depends on the condition of:

- the car (a car with poor brakes or worn tyres can not stop as quickly)
- the road and the weather (a car cannot stop as quickly on a wet road or in the rain)

- the driver (a driver who is tired or distracted, or who has been taking alcohol or other drugs, e.g. some medicines, has slower reactions).

Question

9 Which of the factors above affect thinking distance, and which affect braking distance?

Friction and motion

When an object moves through a **fluid** (a gas or liquid), there is friction between the object and the fluid, e.g.

- **air resistance** as a car drives through the air
- water resistance as a fish swims through water.

The frictional force acts in the opposite direction to the object's motion. The faster the object moves, the greater the frictional force.

When a vehicle travels at a steady speed, the driving force (forwards) balances the frictional forces (backwards). The resultant is zero – that's why the vehicle's speed is steady.

Terminal velocity

The following diagram shows a parachutist falling through the air.

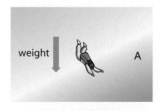

A	- weight acts downwards - the parachutist starts falling faster and faster
B	- as the parachutist speeds up, the frictional force of air resistance increases - the resultant downwards force is less - eventually the person is going so fast that the frictional force balances the weight - the parachutist stops speeding up and continues at a steady speed, called **terminal velocity**
C	- the parachute is opened – air resistance suddenly increases a lot - now the resultant force is upwards – the parachutist starts slowing down
D	- as the parachutist slows down, air resistance decreases - eventually, air resistance exactly balances the weight again – this is a new terminal velocity, but slower than before, because the parachute generates more air resistance at a given speed

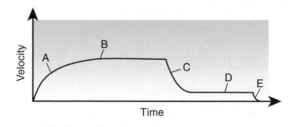

Exam tip

Make sure you can sketch a graph like this and explain the shape of each part.

Remember: when friction force = downwards force, the object does not stop – it falls at a constant velocity.

Question

10 What happens at section E of the graph? Explain your answer.

After revising this section, you should be able...

- to discuss energy transformations involving kinetic energy
- to perform calculations involving forces, work and energy
- to evaluate safety features in terms of momentum
- to calculate the momentum, velocity or mass of an object involved in a collision or explosion

Kinetic energy

An object that is moving has **kinetic energy**. When the object speeds up or slows down, energy is transformed.

Question

1 Copy and complete the table below.

car speeding up			kinetic
ball rolling down hill		...transformed into...	kinetic
ball hitting a wall	kinetic		
wind turbine turning	kinetic		

An object's kinetic energy depends on:

- its mass
- its speed.

$$\text{kinetic energy (joule, J)} = \frac{1}{2} \times \text{mass (kg)} \times (\text{speed})^2 \ ((\text{m/s})^2)$$

Exam tip

Names of units (e.g. joule, newton) have lowercase letters even if the symbol (e.g. J, N) has a capital letter.

For example:

The kinetic energy of a 1500 kg car travelling at 20 m/s is:

$$\frac{1}{2} \times \text{mass} \times (\text{speed})^2 = \frac{1}{2} \times 1500 \times 20^2$$
$$= 300\,000\,\text{J or } 300\,\text{kJ}$$

Exam tip

Remember: only the speed is squared. It is easiest to enter the numbers into your calculator in this sequence: speed² × ½ × mass.

Question

2 What is the kinetic energy of a 40 kg child running at 4 m/s?

Work

When a force makes an object move or change its shape, we say that **work** is done.

When a force causes an object to move through a distance:

work done (J) = force applied (N) × distance moved in direction of force (m)

For example:

The work done when you lift a 20 N weight by 1.5 m is:

$$\text{force applied} \times \text{distance moved in direction of force} = 20 \times 1.5$$
$$= 30\,\text{J}$$

Exam tip

A force is only doing work if it causes an object to move in the direction of the force.

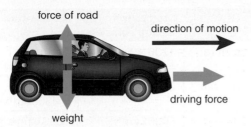

force of road

direction of motion

driving force

weight

▲ The driving force of the car is doing work. The weight is not.

How science works

Like many words, 'work' has a special meaning in science that is different from its everyday meaning.

Question

3 How much work is done by gravity when it causes a 30 N weight to fall by 6 m?

When work is done, energy is transferred.

work done = energy transferred

- Work done against friction is mainly transformed into thermal energy.
- Work done to change the shape of an **elastic** object (one that can recover its original shape) is transformed into **elastic potential energy** which is stored in the object.

Question

4 Give an example of each of the situations listed above.

Momentum

An object:
- with a large mass, or
- which is moving fast

has a lot of **momentum**.

momentum (kg m/s) = mass (kg) × velocity (m/s)

Question

5 What is the momentum of a 3 kg package on a conveyor belt moving at 2 m/s? What about when the conveyor belt stops?

Exam tip

Momentum depends on velocity, so it has a direction. A change in direction will change the momentum.

When a force acts on an object that can move, its momentum changes. The change is related to the force and how long it acts for.

$$\text{force (N)} = \frac{\text{change in momentum (kg m/s)}}{\text{time taken for the change (s)}}$$

Safety features

For a given change in momentum:
- the more time the change takes, the smaller the force required.

How science works

Suggest how the situations in the diagram below follow from the above equation?

▲ A small frictional force with the grass will stop the ball gradually. Stopping it more quickly takes a stronger force.

For example:

A car travelling at 20 m/s collides with a wall. The driver's head, mass 8 kg, hits the dashboard and takes 0.005 s to stop. With what force does the driver's head hit the dashboard?

momentum of head before the collision =
8 × 20 = 160 kg m/s

momentum of head after the collision =
0 kg m/s

$$\text{force} = \frac{\text{change in momentum}}{\text{time taken for change}}$$

$$= \frac{160}{0.005}$$

$$= 32\,000\,\text{N}$$

Safety features like air-bags increase the time taken for momentum to change, so force is less.

For example:

If the car in the example is fitted with an air-bag, the driver's head takes 1.6 s to stop.

force = 160/1.6 = 100 N

Question

6 A 60 kg gymnast falls onto the floor at 2 m/s and stops. (a) The impact with the floor lasts 0.008 s. What force does she experience? (b) With a safety mat, the impact lasts 0.2 s. What force does she experience now?

Collisions and explosions

In a collision or explosion:

- the total momentum afterwards is the same as before, so long as no **external force** acts
- we say that momentum is **conserved**.

For example:

A 1200 kg green car travelling north at 5 m/s collides with a stationary silver car of mass 1500 kg. The silver car starts moving north at 3 m/s. How fast does the green car move after the collision?

	Momentum before collision	Momentum after collision
green car	1200 × 5 = 6000 kg m/s	?
silver car	0	1500 × 3 = 4500 kg m/s
total	6000 kg m/s	6000 kg m/s

Momentum is conserved, so the total momentum after the collision must be the same as before.

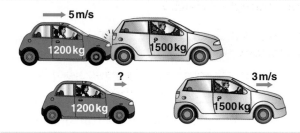

After the collision:

momentum of green car = 6000 − 4500
= 1500 kg m/s

$$\text{So velocity of green car} = \frac{\text{momentum}}{\text{mass}}$$

$$= \frac{1500}{1200}$$

$$= 1.25\,\text{m/s north}$$

Exam tip

If a momentum or a velocity turns out to be negative, that means the object is moving in the opposite direction from the direction you defined as positive.

Questions

7 A ball of mass 2 kg travelling to the right at 5 m/s hits a stationary ball of mass 6 kg. The 6 kg ball moves off to the right at 2.5 m/s. What happens to the 2 kg ball?

8 A stationary firework explodes into two fragments. One has a mass of 0.2 kg and moves off to the left at 20 m/s. The other moves off to the right at 16 m/s. What is its mass?

Static electricity

An electrical **insulator** is a material that does not conduct electricity.

When you rub certain insulators against each other, they become electrically charged.

- Negatively charged electrons are rubbed off one material onto the other.
- The material that gains electrons gets a negative charge.
- The other material is left with an equal positive charge.

The charges are not flowing and are called **static electricity**.

Exam tip

Atoms, electrons and charges are covered in C2 1 Atoms build matter, page 20.

Remember: only electrons move. Positive charges do not move from one object to another – they result from electrons moving away.

Question

1 Huan becomes positively charged by rubbing her shoes on the carpet. Explain in terms of electrons how this works.

Attraction and repulsion

Charged objects exert a force on each other. Objects with:

- the same type of charge repel
- opposite types of charge attract.

This can be useful, e.g. for spray painting cars or bicycle frames.

- All the paint droplets are given one type of charge. They repel each other and do not clump together.
- The car or bicycle is given the opposite type of charge. The paint is attracted evenly all over it.

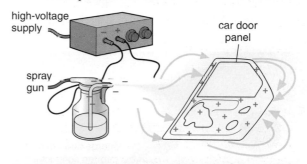

Question

2 When Huan is charged her hair sticks out. Why does this happen?

Charge and potential difference

The greater the charge on an object, the greater the **potential difference (p.d.)** or voltage between the object and the earth.

If the p.d. is high enough, a spark can jump between the object and the earth. The spark is a sudden flow of electricity. This makes the object **discharge** (lose its charge). For example:

- lightning is a huge spark between the earth and a highly charged thundercloud, or between two clouds.

A spark can also jump between the object and a **conductor** connected to earth. For example:

- a metal lightning rod on a building – the lightning jumps to the rod and is conducted to earth.

A charged object can be **earthed** – connected directly to the earth using a conductor. Charge flows through the conductor and the object discharges safely without a spark.

Metals make good conductors because their electrons are free to move around and carry charge.

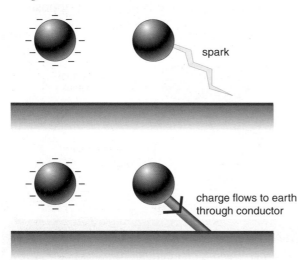

spark

charge flows to earth through conductor

Dangerous static

Materials that can become charged to a high p.d. and cause sparks include:

- fuel flowing through a pipe when a lorry or an aeroplane is refuelled
- grain flowing through a chute
- paper passing through rollers in a factory.

Sparks can be dangerous because they can light the flammable material (fuel, grain or paper) and cause a fire.

To protect against this, a conductor is used to discharge the charged objects safely. For example:

- the fuel pipe, the chute or the rollers are connected to the earth with a metal wire.

Question

3 In hospital operations, a drug used to make the patient unconscious is an explosive gas. Explain why the floor of the operating theatre is designed to conduct electricity.

Useful static

Electrostatic charges can be useful, e.g. in:

- smoke precipitators
- photocopiers.

Smoke precipitator

Power stations that burn fossil fuels produce smoke containing tiny solid particles of soot and dust. A smoke **precipitator** removes these particles, reducing pollution.

- The precipitator contains a grid of wires charged to a high negative voltage followed by collecting plates charged to a high positive voltage.
- As the smoke particles pass the wires, they pick up electrons and become negatively charged.
- As the particles pass the collecting plates, they are attracted to the positive charge.
- Dust builds up on the plates. It can be removed periodically by knocking the plates.

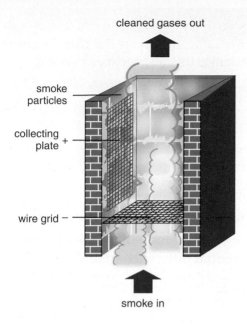

cleaned gases out

smoke particles

collecting plate +

wire grid −

smoke in

Photocopier

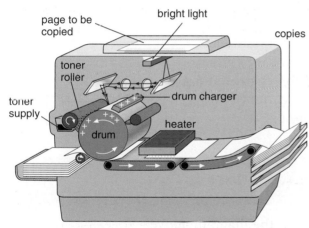

page to be copied

bright light

copies

toner roller

drum charger

toner supply

heater

drum

It is easier to understand what happens in a photocopier if we imagine the drum as a flat sheet.

1 The drum is sprayed with positive charge.

2 A bright light shines on the page to be copied. The light reflects off the white areas and is focused onto the drum. Where light falls, the charges on the drum are given enough energy to flow to earth. Charges in the dark areas remain stuck to the drum.

3 Particles of solid ink called 'toner' are given a negative charge. They are attracted to the positive areas of the drum.

4 A piece of paper is given a positive charge and pressed against the drum. It attracts the negatively charged toner.

5 The paper is heated (see the diagram). This melts the toner and sticks it to the paper.

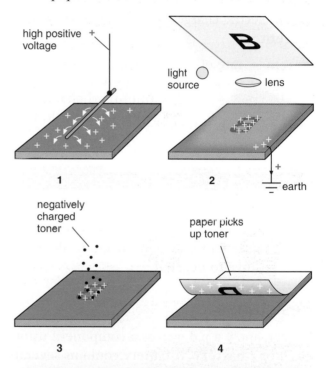

high positive voltage +

light source

lens

1

2

earth +

negatively charged toner

paper picks up toner

3

4

Question

4 *The drum is an insulator. What would happen to the charges in the dark areas of the image if the drum were made from conducting material?*

How science works

The previous diagram shows the photocopier drum being sprayed with positive charges because this shows simply how the drum becomes charged. But, in fact, it is negatively charged electrons that move. Explain how the movement of electrons gives the drum a positive charge.

After revising this section, you should be able...

- to draw and interpret circuit diagrams
- to explain how given circuits work
- to use oscilloscope traces to find the p.d. of d.c. supplies, and the peak p.d. and frequency of a.c. supplies
- to recognise unsafe practices in wiring plugs and in the use of mains electricity

Charge and current

When electric charges move, they form a **current**.

current = rate of flow of electric charge

$$\text{current (amp, A)} = \frac{\text{amount of charge flowing (\textbf{coulomb}, C)}}{\text{time (seconds, s)}}$$

Question

1 *Eight coulombs of charge flow through a circuit in four seconds. What is the current?*

We show current on circuit diagrams flowing from positive to negative.

Resistance

We can apply a p.d. across a component using a cell or a **battery**. A battery contains several cells connected in **series** (end-to-end).

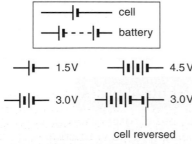

———┤├——	cell
——┤├ - - -┤├—	battery

——┤├— 1.5 V   ——┤│┤├— 4.5 V

——┤│├— 3.0 V   ——┤│┤┤├— 3.0 V

cell reversed

▲ The p.d.s of cells add up when they are connected in series.

Resistance is a measure of how easy it is for current to flow through a component when a p.d. is applied.

The higher the resistance:

- the harder it is for current to flow
- the less current will flow for a given potential difference (p.d.).

$$\begin{array}{lcl}\text{potential difference (volt, V)} & = & \text{current (A)} \times \begin{array}{l}\text{resistance} \\ \textbf{(ohm, } \Omega\textbf{)}\end{array}\end{array}$$

Measuring resistance

To find resistance, we measure the p.d. across the **resistor** and the current flowing through it.

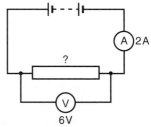

$$\text{resistance} = \frac{\text{p.d.}}{\text{current}}$$

So in the diagram above:

$$\text{resistance} = \frac{6}{2} = 3\,\Omega$$

Questions

2 *A 1.5 A current flows through a 6 Ω resistor. What is the p.d. across the resistor?*

3 *A p.d. of 6 V is applied across a 24 Ω resistor. What current flows?*

We can change p.d. using a variable power supply.

If the positive and negative terminals are reversed so that current flows the other way, we describe p.d. and current as negative.

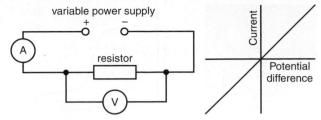

▲ The current in a resistor is directly proportional to the p.d. applied.

Resistance of a filament lamp

Current is not directly proportional to p.d. for all components.

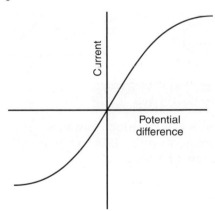

▲ Current–p.d. graph for a filament lamp.

As the p.d. gets larger, it becomes harder to increase the current. The resistance of the lamp increases because:

- electrons making up the current collide with atoms of the filament and make them vibrate more
- the more the atoms are vibrating, the harder it is for the current to get through.

The extra vibration also means that the filament heats up.

Components in series and parallel

For components (e.g. resistors) in series:

- the current is the same through all the components
- the total p.d. of the supply is shared between the components
- the total resistance is the sum of the individual resistances.

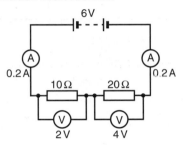

▲ Total resistance is $10\,\Omega + 20\,\Omega = 30\,\Omega$.

For components in **parallel**:

- the p.d. across each component is the same
- the total current is the sum of the currents in the individual components.

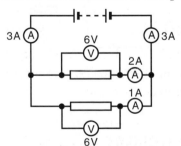

Question

4 Copy the circuits below and fill in the missing p.d. and current values.

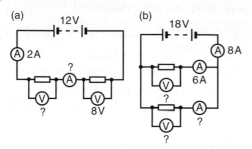

How science works

You should also be able to work out all the resistances in the question above. Can you see how? Calculate them.

The variable resistor

A **variable resistor** is a resistor whose resistance can be changed.

It is useful, e.g. for dimming lamps.

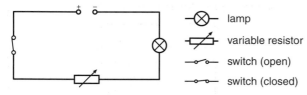

lamp

variable resistor

switch (open)

switch (closed)

▲ As the resistance increases, the current falls and the lamp gets dimmer.

The thermistor

A **thermistor** is a type of resistor whose resistance goes down when it gets hot.

It is useful, e.g. in automatic fire alarms. When the temperature goes up, resistance falls and the current in the thermistor rises. This triggers the alarm.

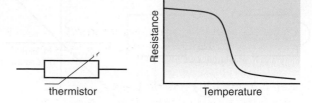

thermistor

Temperature

The light-dependent resistor

A **light-dependent resistor (LDR)** is a type of resistor whose resistance goes down in bright light.

It is useful, e.g. in lamps that turn on automatically at night. When it gets dark, resistance rises and the current through the LDR falls. This triggers the lamp.

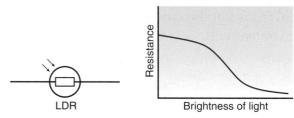

LDR

Brightness of light

How science works

Suggest a way of using resistance measurements on an LDR to measure the brightness of a lamp.

The diode

A **diode** lets current flow only in one direction.

If the power supply is reversed so that the p.d. across the diode is negative, the resistance is extremely high so almost no current flows.

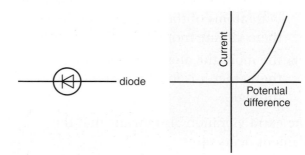

diode

Current

Potential difference

A.c. and d.c.

Cells and batteries supply **direct current (d.c.)**, which flows steadily in one direction. Mains electricity is **alternating current (a.c.)**. Its direction keeps reversing.

We can see the difference using an **oscilloscope**.

On an oscilloscope trace:

- time goes from left to right
- p.d. goes up (for positive) and down (for negative)
- the centre line represents 0 V.

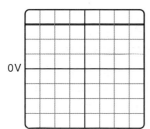

▲ A d.c. trace.   ▲ An a.c. trace.

The scales of the trace can be adjusted. When you interpret a trace, you need to know:

- how much time each horizontal square represents
- how many volts each vertical square represents.

For example:

If the p.d. scale of the d.c. trace is set to 5 V per square, then p.d. = 3 squares = 15 V.

Question

5 *If the p.d. scale of the a.c. trace in the diagram is set to 2 V per square, what maximum p.d. does it reach?*

We can use an oscilloscope to measure the **frequency** of an a.c. voltage.

$$\text{frequency (hertz, Hz)} = \frac{1}{\text{time for complete wave (s)}}$$

For example:

If the timescale of the a.c. trace above is set to 0.02 s per square, then time taken for complete wave = 4 squares = 0.08 s.

$$\text{frequency} = \frac{1}{0.08}$$

$$= 12.5 \, \text{Hz}$$

Question

6 *In the oscilloscope trace below, one vertical square represents 10 V and one horizontal square represents 0.05 s. What is (a) the peak voltage, (b) the frequency?*

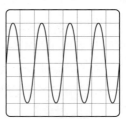

Mains electricity

Mains electricity is an a.c. supply, with three terminals:

- Live (**a** on the diagram on page 52) – p.d. alternates between positive and negative with respect to the neutral terminal.
- Neutral (**b** on the diagram on page 52) – p.d. stays close to zero with respect to earth.
- Earth – connected to the Earth, voltage zero.

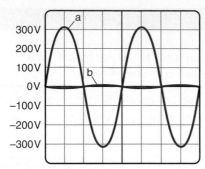

It is hard to describe the voltage of an a.c. supply because it keeps changing. We usually give a kind of average value. For the mains in the UK:

- average voltage is about 230 V
- frequency is about 50 Hz.

Mains wiring

Each wire is attached to one terminal of the plug:

- **Live** – brown.
- **Neutral** – blue.
- **Earth** – green and yellow.

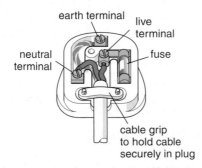

earth terminal, live terminal

neutral terminal, fuse

cable grip to hold cable securely in plug

earth pin longer than other pins – when plug is pushed in, appliance is connected to earth before live supply

casing made of insulating material (plastic or rubber)

pins made of brass, a conductor which is strong and does not corrode

plastic to protect you if you touch the live or neutral pin

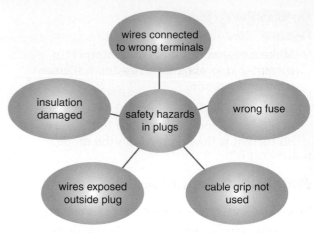

wires connected to wrong terminals

insulation damaged

safety hazards in plugs

wrong fuse

wires exposed outside plug

cable grip not used

The spider diagram shows some safety hazards of plugs. Other electrical safety hazards include:

- using too many plugs in one socket – this draws a large current, which can create enough heat to start a fire
- using electricity with wet skin – wet skin is a better conductor than dry skin, so any electric shock is likely to be more harmful.

Fuses and earthing

The earth wire and the **fuse** are safety features. If an appliance develops a fault so that a live wire touches the outer casing, it can give you an electric shock that might be fatal.

If a fault like this develops:

1 The charge on the case flows to the Earth through the earth wire.

2 This creates a large current.

3 As the current passes through the fuse, it heats the fuse wire so much that it melts.

4 This breaks the circuit and stops the electricity from flowing.

Exam tip

Draw a diagram showing the process above.

Only appliances with metal casings can become 'live' in this way. Appliances with insulated plastic casings do not need an earth wire. They are usually wired with a cable containing only live and neutral wires.

We also use fuses, or similar devices called circuit breakers, in houses to protect the mains supply.

Choosing the right fuse

Fuses are labelled to show how much current they can withstand, e.g. 3 A, 5 A or 13 A.

 fuse

A fuse must withstand the normal current in the device, but melt if the current gets much higher. The rating of a fuse should be a bit more than the normal current in the device, but not much more.

Question

7 Why should the rating of the fuse be more than the normal current in the device but not much more?

Energy and power

When a p.d. makes charge flow through a resistor, electrical energy is transformed into thermal energy.

$$\text{energy transformed (J)} = \text{potential difference (V)} \times \text{charge (C)}$$

How science works

How is the electrical → thermal energy transformation used in (a) a light bulb, (b) a fuse?

The rate of energy transformation is called **power**.

$$\text{power (W)} = \frac{\text{energy transformed (J)}}{\text{time taken (s)}}$$

Electrical devices often have a label to show their power rating.

Questions

8 An electric fire transforms 30 kJ in 15 s. What is its power?

9 How much energy does a 1500 W toaster transform in 60 seconds?

Power and current

We can calculate the power of a device from the p.d. across the device and the current flowing through it.

$$\text{power (\textbf{watt}, W)} = \text{potential difference (V)} \times \text{current (A)}$$

We can rearrange this equation to find the current in a device from its power rating and the p.d. This enables us to choose a suitable fuse.

Questions

10 What power is generated when a p.d. of 9 V makes a current of 3 A flow through a resistor?

11 What current flows in a 720 W microwave when it is attached to the mains at 240 V? Which fuse should be chosen: 2 A, 5 A or 13 A?

Exam tip

Draw a table showing circuit symbols and properties for: voltmeter, ammeter, cell, battery, resistor, lamp, variable resistor, thermistor, LDR, diode, fuse.

After revising this section, you should be able…

- to explain how the plum pudding model of the atom was replaced by the nuclear model
- to explain and predict the effect of alpha and beta decay on radioactive nuclei
- to explain and give examples of nuclear fission, including chain reactions, and nuclear fusion

For this section, you need to remember some content from C2 1 Atoms build matter (page 20) and C2 2 The power of measurement (page 24).

- All atoms of a given element have the same number of protons ('atomic number').
- Atoms of different elements have different numbers of protons.
- Atoms of the same element with different numbers of neutrons are called isotopes.
- In an uncharged atom, the number of electrons equals the number of protons.
- Atoms may gain or lose electrons to form charged particles called ions.
- The total number of protons + neutrons in an atom is called the mass number.

Particle	Charge (relative to proton)	Mass (relative to proton
proton	+1 (positive)	1
neutron	0 (neutral)	1
electron	−1 (negative)	tiny

Models of the atom

Until about 100 years ago, scientists thought that:

- the mass of the atom was distributed through its whole volume
- most of the atom contained positive charge
- tiny particles of negative charge were dotted through the large positive charge.

The **model** resembles a pudding with fruits in it, so it is called the **plum pudding model** of the atom.

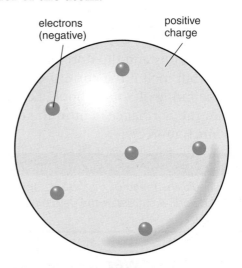

electrons (negative) positive charge

How science works

In those days, scientists knew that atoms contain positive and negative charges, and that the negative charges are tiny compared to atoms. But protons and neutrons had not been discovered. So at the time, the model made sense.

Rutherford's experiment

In 1909, Geiger and Marsden probed atoms by firing alpha particles at a very thin gold foil in a vacuum. They knew that alpha particles are:

- positively charged
- fast-moving
- much smaller than gold atoms.

The plum pudding model predicts that:

- most alpha particles will go straight through the gold (imagine the plum pudding being hit by a bullet)
- some alpha particles will be deflected a little by the positive charge of the atoms.

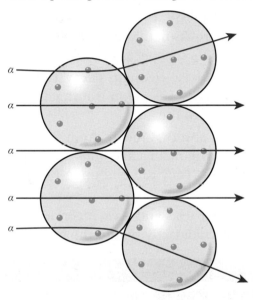

In fact:

- most of the alpha particles went straight through the foil
- some were deflected by various amounts
- most surprisingly, a few were deflected so much that they bounced back off the foil.

There was no way that a plum pudding atom could deflect a fast-moving alpha particle so much.

Geiger and Marsden's boss, Rutherford, suggested a new model of the atom in which:

- the positive charge and most of the mass are concentrated at the centre
- the electrons orbit this central nucleus.

The **nuclear model** explains the results.

- Most of the time, the alpha particle passes far from the nucleus and is hardly deflected.
- Occasionally, the alpha particle passes very close to the nucleus.
- If this happens, the concentrated positive charge can repel the alpha particle backwards.

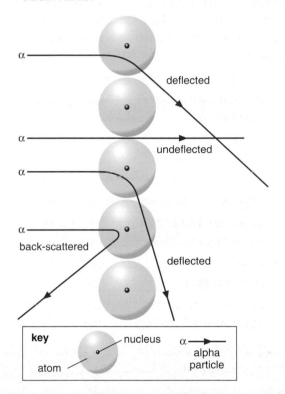

Question

1 Why does an atomic nucleus repel alpha particles?

Radioactivity

Radioactive nuclei are unstable nuclei which emit radiation and become more stable. This is called radioactive **decay**.

Two types of radiation are **alpha particles** and **beta particles**.

Type of radiation	What it is
alpha	two protons + two neutrons
beta	electron

A beta particle is formed when a neutron in the nucleus breaks down into a proton and an electron. The proton remains in the nucleus and the electron is emitted.

Exam tip

Remember: a beta particle is not one of the atom's orbiting electrons. It comes from inside the nucleus.

Question

2 What are the mass and charge of (a) an alpha particle, and (b) a beta particle, relative to a proton?

Type of decay	Effect on atomic number	Effect on neutron number	Effect on mass number
alpha	down by 2	down by 2	down by 4
beta	up by 1	down by 1	stays the same

▲ Radioactive decay can change one element into another.

Question

3 A $^{14}_{6}C$ nucleus emits a beta particle and decays into a nitrogen nucleus. Write the symbol for this nucleus, showing the atomic number and mass number.

Background radiation

There are low levels of radiation all around us, e.g. in:

- air
- rocks and building materials
- food and drink.

This **background radiation** has many sources.

- Cosmic rays are radiation from outer space. Most are absorbed by the atmosphere.
- Some rocks naturally contain radioactive elements such as uranium.
- When these elements decay, the radioactive gas radon is formed. This seeps into the air.
- Plants absorb minerals from the soil, including radioactive ones if they are present. They can end up in human food.
- Nuclear tests and accidents release man-made radioactivity into the environment.

Question

4 Explain why cosmic rays are more intense on top of tall mountains than at sea level.

Nuclear fission

Some nuclei can be made to split by firing neutrons at them. **Nuclear fission** (splitting) releases:

- two smaller nuclei
- two or three neutrons from the large nucleus that don't end up in the smaller nuclei
- energy.

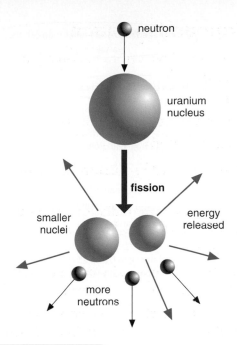

neutron

uranium nucleus

fission

smaller nuclei

energy released

more neutrons

Exam tip

Nuclei hardly ever undergo fission by themselves. They must first absorb a neutron.

Nuclear fission is used in nuclear power stations to generate energy. The usual fuels are uranium-235 and plutonium-239.

The neutrons released by nuclear fission can be absorbed by other large nuclei. This causes more fissions and releases more neutrons, which can cause yet more fissions, and so on. We call this process a **chain reaction**.

Each fission only needs one neutron to get going, but releases two or three. So a chain reaction can get faster and faster, releasing a lot of energy very quickly. This is what happens in a nuclear bomb.

Question

5 Draw a diagram showing a chain reaction

Nuclear fusion

In **nuclear fusion**, two nuclei fuse (join) to make a larger one. The process releases energy. An example is the fusion of two hydrogen nuclei (different isotopes in the diagram) to form a helium nucleus.

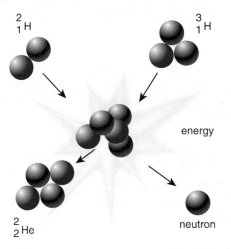

$^2_1$H

$^3_1$H

energy

$^2_2$He

neutron

It is difficult to make nuclei fuse. They must collide with very high energy, otherwise they simply repel each other. Nuclear fusion happens best at:

- high pressure
- high temperature.

Question

6 Explain how (a) high pressure, and (b) high temperature help nuclei to collide with high enough energy to fuse.

Nuclear fusion is the process that releases energy in:

- stars
- hydrogen bombs.

Scientists are working to produce controlled fusion to release energy for power stations.

How science works

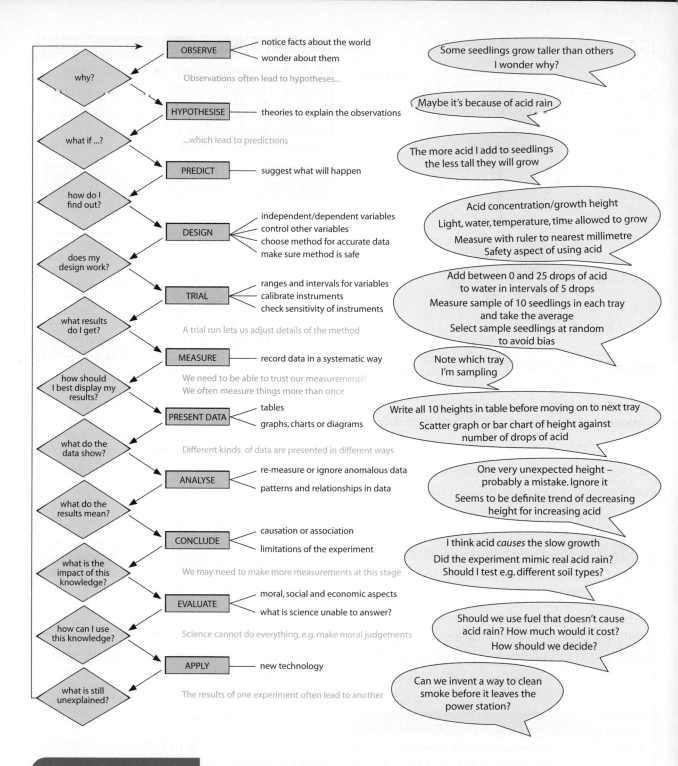

Apply the stages in the flowchart to an investigation of how the rate at which a drink cools depends on what the cup is made of. (Start with the observation that drinks stay warm for longer in some cups than in others.)

ISA

The scientific process requires care. You may be asked about:

- whether the choice of measuring instrument is appropriate
- whether measurements have been repeated a sensible number of times
- whether the method used is able to answer the question
- whether the data allow you to draw a particular conclusion or not
- whether there are likely to be any biases.

Here are some technical terms that you are very likely to be asked about.

Type of data	Description	Example
categoric	data belong in different groups	male/female students
ordered	categoric, but can be ranked	small/medium/large
discrete	data can only be whole numbers	number of plants
continuous	data can be any number	height, weight, time

Question

1 What type of data are (a) the colour of a precipitate (b) the length of a branch?

Description of result	What it means
accurate	the average measurement is very close to the true value
precise	repeated measurements are very similar (but not necessarily accurate!)
reliable	you would get a similar result if you or another person did the measurement again
valid	reliable and also answers the question
anomalous	unexpected, not fitting into the pattern

Question

2 Bill and Jill each measure the mass of a stone three times. Bill's measurements are 92.5 g, 94.0 g and 93.6 g. Jill's are 101 g, 94 g and 97 g. The real mass of the stone is 98 g. Whose results are (a) more accurate (b) more precise?

Type of variable	What it means
independent	the quantity that you deliberately change in the experiment
dependent	the quantity you measure, which may change as you change the independent variable
control	all other variables, which you must keep constant to make the test fair

Question

3 Parveen measures how the p.d. generated by a solar electric cell changes as she changes the area of the cell. (a) What is the independent variable? (b) What is the dependent variable? (c) Give one variable that Parveen must control.

PSA

You will get marks in assessed practicals for good use of scientific methods. This means:

- using a range of equipment without much help
- taking appropriate safety precautions
- taking accurate measurements
- taking measurements in a well-organised way
- writing measurements into a clear table as you take them.

Exam-style questions

1 (a) When we exercise, the temperature of the body increases.

  (i) Explain as fully as you can how the body temperature is returned to normal whilst resting after exercise.

  ....
  ....
  ....
  .... (4 marks)

  (ii) Marathon runners take several drinks during a race to prevent dehydration. Explain how and why dehydration of the body affects body cells.

  ....
  .... (2 marks)

(b) Scientists have developed a device to help people suffering from diabetes. The device monitors the blood sugar concentration and delivers appropriate amounts of insulin into the body.

  (i) Which organ in the body monitors blood sugar concentration?

  .... (1 mark)

  (ii) Describe the effect of insulin on the body.

  ....
  .... (2 marks)

  (iii) Explain the advantage of the new device over twice-daily insulin injections.

  ....
  .... (2 marks)

2 (a) The graph shows the effect of temperature on the rate of photosynthesis.

  (i) Between which temperatures is the rate of photosynthesis fastest?

  .... (1 mark)

  (ii) Suggest why the rate of photosynthesis stays the same between these two temperatures.

  ....
  .... (2 marks)

(b) A greenhouse owner wants to grow lettuces as quickly and cheaply as possible in winter. He decides to use a gas heater.

  Assuming that the fuel costs are identical, what advantage would the gas heater have over electric heating? Explain the reason for your answer.

  ....
  ....(2 marks)

(c) The diagram shows what happens to the energy from grass in part of a field which is grazed by a cow.

  3000 kJ eaten
  100 kJ new growth

  (i) What proportion of the energy from the grass was transferred into new growth?

  ....(1 mark)

  (ii) Describe what happens to the rest of the energy from the grass.

  ....
  .... (2 marks)

(d) Many pigs are reared intensively indoors. Their surroundings are closely controlled so that they have a warm, even temperature. The risk of infection is high but it is reduced by feeding the pigs antibiotics and removing their faeces. The movement of the pigs is restricted.

(i) Explain why farmers keep the pigs at a warm, even temperature.

....

.... *(2 marks)*

(ii) Many people are against the rearing of pigs in the way described above. Explain **two** reasons why.

....

....

....

.... *(4 marks)*

3 (a) Copy and complete the diagram to show how the gender of a child depends on the chromosomes the child inherits from its mother and father.

chromosomes in body cells of mother   chromosomes in body cells of father

XX

chromosomes in eggs   chromosomes in sperms

chromosomes in body cells of daughter   chromosomes in body cells of son

(3 marks)

(b) The diagram below shows the inheritance of Huntington's chorea in a family.

first generation (all over 40 years old)

second generation (all over 40 years old)

third generation (all under 30 years old)

X   Y

Key
■ male showing symptoms of Huntington's chorea
□ male without symptoms of Huntington's chorea
● female showing symptoms of Huntington's chorea
○ female without symptoms of Huntington's chorea

Symptoms of Huntington's chorea usually develop between the ages of 35 and 40.

What is the chance that the following will develop Huntington's chorea?

(i) **X**..

(ii) **Y**..

Explain the reasons for your answers as fully as you can. You may use genetic diagrams if you wish.

(i) ....

....

.... *(3 marks)*

(ii) ....

....

.... *(3 marks)*

(c) Embryos can now be screened for the allele that causes Huntington's chorea.

(i) Give **one** advantage of this technique.

..............................*(1 mark)*

(ii) Explain why some people are against embryo screening.

....

.... *(2 marks)*

4 The following information appears on the label of a packet of antacid tablets:

● Chew the tablets before swallowing for fast relief.

● These tablets neutralise the stomach acids that cause acid indigestion.

● Active ingredients: calcium carbonate and magnesium carbonate.

● Do not take more than 12 tablets in 24 hours.

● If the symptoms persist, seek medical advice.

(a) Explain why chewing the tablets before swallowing will give 'fast relief'.

....

....*(2 marks)*

(b) The equation represents the reaction between calcium carbonate and acid in the stomach.

$CaCO_3$ (s) + ___ HCl (aq) → $CaCl_2$ (aq) + H_2O (l) + CO_2 (g)

(i) Copy the equation, then balance it.

....*(1 mark)*

(ii) Give the meaning of the state symbol (aq).

....*(1 mark)*

(iii) Calculate the mass of carbon dioxide that would be produced when 2 g of calcium carbonate reacts completely with hydrochloric acid. (A_r: Ca = 40; C = 12; O = 16)

Show your working.

(3 marks)

Alison wanted to investigate how quickly the tablets react with excess hydrochloric acid. This is the method she used.

1 50 cm³ of dilute hydrochloric acid were placed in a conical flask.

2 The flask was placed on a digital balance.

3 Ten antacid tablets were dropped into the flask.

4 The apparatus was weighed immediately.

5 The mass of the flask plus its contents was recorded every half minute for 5 minutes.

Alison's results are shown on the graph.

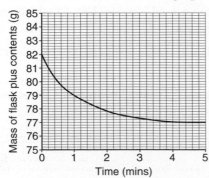

(c) **(i)** What was the sensitivity of the balance in this experiment?

....*(1 mark)*

(ii) What mass of carbon dioxide was given off to the atmosphere in this experiment?

....*(1 mark)*

(d) **(i)** Describe how the rate of the reaction changed during the experiment.

....

.... *(2 marks)*

(ii) Explain why the rate of the reaction changes in this way.

....

.... *(2 marks)*

5 Aluminium oxide is an ionic compound.

(a) Using information from the Data Sheet, copy and complete the drawing of the electronic structure of:

(i) an oxygen atom.

(1 mark)

(ii) an aluminium ion.

(2 marks)

(b) Use information from the Data Sheet to help you to work out the formula of aluminium oxide.

....*(1 mark)*

(c) Explain why aluminium oxide has a very high melting point.

....

.... *(2 marks)*

(d) To make aluminium, aluminium oxide is melted and then electricity is passed through it.

  (i) Why must the aluminium oxide be melted before electricity will pass through it?

  ....

  .... *(2 marks)*

  (ii) Complete the half equation below to show how aluminium is formed in the cell.

  $Al^{3+} +$ ___ $e^- \rightarrow Al$ *(1 mark)*

(e) Explain how the structure of aluminium allows it to conduct electricity.

....

.... *(2 marks)*

6 The Haber process is used to make ammonia (NH_3) which is an important substance. The equation shows the reaction in which ammonia is formed.

N_2 (g) + $3H_2$ (g) $\rightleftharpoons$ $2NH_3$ (g) + heat

The graph shows how temperature and pressure affect how much ammonia is produced in the reaction.

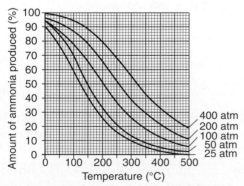

In the industrial process a mixture of nitrogen and hydrogen is passed over iron at a temperature of about 450°C and 200 atmospheres pressure.

(a) Explain why the nitrogen and hydrogen mixture is passed over iron.

....

.... *(2 marks)*

(b) Using information from the graph, explain, as fully as you can, why 450°C and 200 atmospheres were chosen as the conditions for this process.

....

....

....

....

....

.... *(6 marks)*

7 A family car has a mass of 1000 kg. The car will accelerate from 0 to 30 m/s in 10 seconds. It has a maximum speed of 150 km/h.

(a) **(i)** Calculate the acceleration of the car during the 10 seconds.

        (2 marks)

  (ii) Calculate the force needed to produce this acceleration.

        (2 marks)

  (iii) Explain why this car cannot travel at more than 150 km/h.

  ....

  ....

  .... *(3 marks)*

(b) The car is involved in a collision.

  (i) Explain why the driver tends to be thrown towards the windscreen during a collision.

  ....

  ....*(2 marks)*

(ii) During the collision the front end of the car becomes crumpled and buckled.

Explain how a crumple zone on a car helps to save a driver from serious injury.

....

....*(2 marks)*

(iii) The car was travelling at 30 m/s immediately before the crash. Calculate the energy which has to be dissipated as the front of the car crumples.

(3 marks)

8 The graph shows how the current through a 230 V lamp changes in the first second after it is switched on. It takes 0.5 seconds for the filament to reach its normal operating temperature.

(a) Describe how the resistance of the lamp changes after the lamp is switched on.

....

....

.... *(3 marks)*

(b) Calculate the resistance of the filament whilst the lamp is drawing the maximum current.

(3 marks)

(c) Calculate the power taken by the lamp at its normal operating current.

(2 marks)

(d) Calculate the energy used by the lamp in one hour of normal use.

(3 marks)

9 (a) Describe the 'plum pudding' model of the atom.

....

.... *(2 marks)*

(b) Rutherford fired alpha particles at gold leaf. The diagram shows the paths of two alpha particles **A** and **B** into and out of the gold leaf.

Explain the paths taken by particles **A** and **B**.

....

....

.... *(3 marks)*

(c) Describe the model of the atom which Rutherford derived from this experiment.

....

....

.... *(3 marks)*

Answers to exam-style questions

1 (a) (i) sweat produced *(1)* evaporation of sweat takes heat from body *(1)* blood vessels supplying skin capillaries dilate *(1)* more heat lost by radiation *(1)*

(ii) body cells lose water by osmosis *(1)* because body fluids are now more concentrated than body cells *(1)*

(b) (i) pancreas *(1)*

(ii) lowers blood sugar concentration *(1)* by increasing uptake of sugar by cells / stimulating action of enzymes that convert sugar into glycogen *(1)*

(iii) blood sugar concentration more stable *(1)* because insulin delivery responds to blood sugar concentration *(1)*

2 (a) (i) 21°C and 27°C *(1)*

(ii) some other factor is limiting *(1)* e.g. carbon dioxide *(1)*

(b) greater rate of growth *(1)* because the gas heater gives off carbon dioxide *(1)*

(c) (i) $\frac{1}{30}$ / 0.03 / 3.3% *(1)*

(ii) some lost in faeces *(1)* some lost via respiration *(1)*

(d) (i) to minimise heat loss from the animals *(1)* greater proportion of food converted to muscle (meat) *(1)*

(ii) e.g. reference to 'cruelty' / unnatural conditions *(1)* meat may contain antibiotics which may affect human health / lead to resistant strains *(1)*

3 (a)

father correct *(1)* gametes all correct *(1)* daughter and son both correct *(1)*

(b) (i) no chance *(1)* because neither parent has the disorder *(1)* so cannot have Huntington allele *(1)*

(ii) 50% *(1)* because mother has Huntington allele *(1)* but mother has only one Huntington allele because her mother did not have Huntington's chorea

(c) (i) allows parents to decide if they wish to continue pregnancy if the child has Huntington allele *(1)*

(ii) may involve killing embryos with the Huntington allele *(1)* some people think this is murder / some people believe that human life begins at conception not birth *(1)*

4 (a) rate of reaction increased *(1)* because reactant has greater surface area *(1)*

(b) (i) $2HCl$ *(1)*

(ii) in aqueous solution *(1)*

(iii) M_r of calcium carbonate (40 + 12 + 48) = 100; M_r of carbon dioxide (12 + 32) = 44 *(1)* 44 × (2/100) *(1)* = 0.88 g *(1)*

(c) (i) 0.1 g / 0.2 g *(1)*

    (ii) 5 g *(1)*

(d) (i) falls rapidly at first *(1)* then falls to zero *(1)*

    (ii) as reactant is used up *(1)* there are fewer particles to react *(1)*

5 (a) (i)

six outer electrons *(1)*

    (ii)

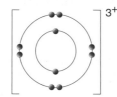

eight outer electrons *(1)* 3+ in correct position *(1)*

(b) Al_2O_3 *(1)*

(c) strong forces of attraction *(1)* between oppositely charged particles / ions *(1)*

(d) (i) ions break free from ionic structure *(1)* current carried by movement of ions *(1)*

    (ii) $3e^-$ *(1)*

(e) some outer electrons delocalised *(1)* movement of these carries current *(1)*

6 (a) iron is catalyst *(1)* this increases rate of reaction *(1)*

(b) any six from: high pressure increases yield *(1)* because less reactant molecules *(1)* but high pressure increases cost / safety risk *(1)* low temperature increases yield *(1)* because exothermic reaction *(1)* but at low temperature rate is slow /

catalyst does not work *(1)* optimum conditions needed to balance rate and percentage yield *(1)* rate is slow (at higher temperature) so need a catalyst *(1)* low percentage conversion so recycle untreated gases *(1)*

7 (a) (i) $(30\,m/s - 0\,m/s)/10\,s$ *(1)* = $3\,m/s^2$ *(1)*

    (ii) $1000\,kg \times 3\,m/s^2$ *(1)* = $3000\,N$ *(1)*

    (iii) friction increases with speed *(1)* until frictional force equals driving force *(1)* acceleration then equals zero *(1)*

(b) (i) car's momentum destroyed by collision *(1)* but driver still has momentum *(1)*

    (ii) crumple zone squashes up, which absorbs impact *(1)* passenger compartment rides over this zone, coming to a halt more slowly than rest of car *(1)*

    (iii) $\frac{1}{2} \times 1000\,kg \times (30\,m/s)^2$ *(1)* = $450\,000$ *(1)* J *(1)*

8 (a) rises to 0.41 A *(1)* falls rapidly *(1)* levels off at 0.2 A *(1)*

(b) $230\,V/0.41\,A$ *(1)* = 585.4 *(1)* Ω *(1)*

(c) $230\,V \times 0.2\,A$ *(1)* = $46\,W$ *(1)*

(d) $46\,W \times 3600\,s$ *(1)* = $1\,656\,000$ *(1)* J *(1)*

9 (a) pudding: large sphere of positive charge *(1)* plums: negatively charged electrons *(1)*

(b) A goes straight through because most of atom is empty space *(1)* B repelled by opposite *(1)* positive charge in atom *(1)*

(c) most of mass concentrated *(1)* in positively charged nucleus *(1)* around which electrons orbit at a distance *(1)*

Answers to in-text questions

B2 1 Cells and photosynthesis (page 2)

1

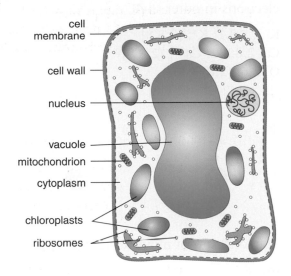

cell membrane

cell wall

nucleus

vacuole

mitochondrion

cytoplasm

chloroplasts

ribosomes

2 Nucleus, both, contains genetic information; vacuole, plant, contains cell sap to help support the cell; chloroplast, plant, contains chlorophyll for photosynthesis; mitochondrion, both, carries out respiration; cell wall, plant, makes cell stronger; ribosome, both, makes proteins; cytoplasm, both, site of most of cell's chemical reactions.

3 Xylem – long and waterproof for transport, rigid for support; phloem – long for transport through whole plant; guard cells – surround pores and change shape to make pores open and close; white blood cells – size and flexibility let them surround bacterial cells; muscle – change in length causes movement; motor neurone – branched to receive chemicals from many relay neurones, long to carry impulse to distant effector; sperm – streamlined and able to move tail for propulsion.

4 Diffusion from blood to cell.

5 Water enters both cells by osmosis. Plant cell is stronger because of cell wall.

6 Light; CO_2; chlorophyll.

7 A different factor is limiting the rate of photosynthesis. The rate cannot increase till we change that factor.

8 Temperature was not limiting.

B2 2 Energy in ecosystems (page 6)

1 Nettle.

2 1%

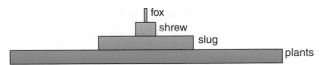

fox

shrew

slug

plants

3 16%

4 They use a lot of energy maintaining a constant body temperature.

5 **(a)** 0.012.

(b) 0.0020.

(c) 0.00023.

(d) 0.000013.

6 Energy is wasted at each stage in the chain so it's more efficient to be a primary consumer than a secondary consumer.

7 Aerobic respiration.

8 More oxygen lets microbes respire faster so they can break down sewage faster.

B2 3 Enzymes and homeostasis (page 10)

1 The substrate no longer fits.

2 A – stomach; B – small intestine.

3 They make it by photosynthesis.

4 Amylase in saliva breaks starch down into sugar.

5 The enzymes start to denature.

6 His intestine will contain a lower water concentration (more salt) so water will leave his cells by osmosis.

7 Make them work less quickly.

8 It would make their blood glucose level too low.

B2 4 Inheriting disease (page 15)

1 Because some of them are enzymes.

2 It does not reduce the number of chromosomes.

3 The offspring gets some genes from each parent, not a full set from either parent.

4 (a) S (smooth).

(b) Ss.

5 (a) Red.

(b)

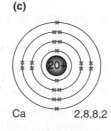

	female	
	R	r
R	RR	Rr
r	Rr	rr

male

(c) No. The expected proportion of 3 red:1 white is only an average over large samples.

6 Genes; alleles.

7 Recessive; if it were dominant, at least one parent would show signs of the disease.

C2 1 Atoms build matter (page 20)

1 Zero; same number of electrons as protons.

2

  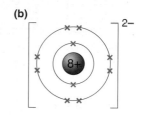

(a) C 2,4 (b) P 2,8,5 (c) Ca 2,8,8,2

3 Periods 1, 2, 3, 4; Energy level of outer electron 1, 2, 3, 4; 1, 2, 3, 4, 5, 6, 7 electrons in outer shell.

4 K: 2,8,8,1; K⁺: [2,8,8]⁺
Ca: 2,8,8,2; Ca²⁺: [2,8,8]²⁺
O: 2,6; [2,8]²⁻
Cl: 2,8,7; Cl⁻; [2,8,8]⁻

5

(a) $[9+]^-$ (b) $[8+]^{2-}$

6 The ions cannot move around.

7 (a) 8

(b) 8

(c) 2

8 Silicon dioxide – giant lattice; rhodium – metal.

C2 2 The power of measurement (page 24)

1 (a) six protons, eight neutrons.

(b) $^{35}_{17}Cl$

2 (a) 3

(b) 9

3 (a) 17

(b) 159.6

4 82.4%

5 28 g CaO and 22 g CO_2

6 CuO method has better atom economy (50% for CuS method).

7 90%

C2 3 The tortoise or the hare (page 28)

1

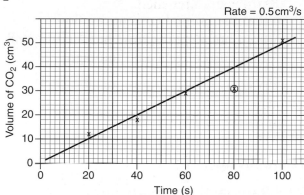

2 Increased rate: concentration of one of reactants (CO_2) is increasing.

3 Dust has a far larger area of exposed surface.

4 1 g – it is a catalyst and not used up in the reaction. He may get a bit less in real life because he may leave some in the beaker, funnel, etc.

C2 4 The energy bank (page 31)

1 Methane + oxygen → carbon dioxide + water;

hydrochloric acid + potassium hydroxide → potassium chloride + water;

zinc + oxygen → zinc oxide.

2 $C + O_2 → CO_2$

3 $ZnCO_3 \xrightarrow{\text{heat}} ZnO + CO_2$

4 If both directions were exothermic, you could create energy from nowhere by doing the reaction repeatedly back and forth. Similarly, if both directions were endothermic, you would be destroying energy.

5 Low temperature, slow, high yield, low cost; high temperature, fast, low yield, high cost; low pressure, slow, low yield, low cost; high pressure, fast, high yield, high cost.

6 Pressure is high enough to give good rate and yield; any higher would be too expensive. Temperature is high enough to give good rate; any higher would give too low a yield and be too expensive.

C2 5 Separating ions for materials (page 34)

1 **(a)** $Mg^{2+} + 2e^- → Mg$, $2Cl^- → Cl_2 + 2e^-$

(b) Cl^- is oxidised, Mg^{2+} is reduced.

2 Hydrogen: less reactive than sodium; chlorine: halogen.

3 $10\,cm^3$; the balanced equation tells you that you need the same number of moles; this is the same volume, as the concentrations are the same.

4 $Mg\,(s) + 2HNO_3\,(aq) → Mg(NO_3)_2\,(aq) + H_2\,(g)$

5 **(a)** Sodium hydroxide + nitric acid

(b) Calcium hydroxide + hydrochloric acid

(c) Magnesium oxide + sulfuric acid

(d) Magnesium iodide + lead nitrate

P2 1 Forces and motion (page 37)

1 0 m/s; 6 m/s

2 $0\,m/s^2$; $-0.4\,m/s^2$

3 240 m; 180 m

4 400 N

5 1.6 N/kg

6 12 N upwards.

7 45 N

8 $5\,m/s^2$ downwards.

9 Condition of driver affects thinking distance; condition of car and road affect braking distance.

10 The parachutist hits the ground: rapid decrease in velocity to zero.

P2 2 Energy and motion (page 42)

1 Chemical – kinetic; potential – kinetic; kinetic – potential, sound, thermal; kinetic – electrical, sound.

2 320 J

3 180 J

4 Rubbing hands to warm them up; pulling a catapult.

5 6 kg m/s; 0

6 (a) 15 000 N

   (b) 600 N

7 It rebounds at 2.5 m/s to the left.

8 0.25 kg

P2 3 Electric charge (page 45)

1 The carpet rubs electrons off her shoes, leaving the carpet negative and Huan positive.

2 Hairs all positive so they repel each other.

3 Otherwise the trolleys, people, etc. could become charged and then discharge with a spark which could light the gas.

4 Charge would even out all over the drum so the image would be lost.

P2 4 Using electricity (page 48)

1 2 A

2 9 V

3 0.25 A

4 (a) 4 V, 2 A

   (b) 18 V in each, 2 A

5 5 V

6 (a) 30 V

   (b) 10 Hz

7 So that the normal current can flow without breaking the fuse, but the fuse will break if current gets a bit too high.

8 2 kW

9 90 kJ

10 27 W

11 3 A; 5 A fuse.

P2 5 Radioactivity (page 54)

1 Both have positive charge.

2 (a) 4, +2

   (b) tiny, −1

3 $^{14}_{7}\text{N}$

4 Less energy has been absorbed by the atmosphere.

5

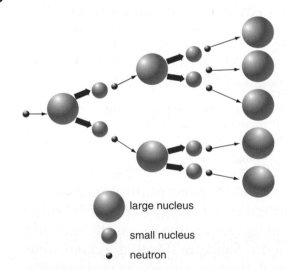

large nucleus

small nucleus

neutron

6 (a) Nuclei are forced closer together.

   (b) Nuclei are moving around with more energy.

Glossary and index

acceleration The rate of change of velocity. Page 38

activation energy The energy needed to start a reaction, used to break bonds. Page 28

aerobic respiration Chemical reactions in cells which use glucose and oxygen to release energy. Carbon dioxide and water are produced as waste products. Page 11

air resistance The drag force on an object moving through the air; a form of friction. Page 41

alleles Different forms of the same gene. Page 16

alpha particle Two protons and two neutrons – the same as a helium nucleus. Page 55

alternating current (a.c.) Current which flows in one direction and then the other, constantly reversing. Page 51

amino acids The basic units from which proteins are made. Page 5

amylase A type of digestive enzyme which breaks down starch into glucose. Page 11

asexual reproduction Reproduction that does not involve the formation of gametes. Page 15

atom The smallest part of an element that still has the properties of that element. Page 20

atom economy How much useful product is produced in a reaction compared with the total mass of atoms used. Page 26

atomic number (Z) The number of protons in an atom; same as the proton number. Page 20

background radiation We are exposed to background radiation all the time, from radioactive substances around us and from cosmic rays. Page 56

base A chemical (such as a metal oxide or hydroxide) that can neutralise an acid. Page 36

battery Two or more cells connected end-to-end to give a bigger p.d. Page 48

beta particle An electron emitted from the nucleus of an atom during radioactive decay. Page 55

biomass The mass of living organisms in an area. Page 6

braking distance The distance travelled by a car while the brakes are applied. Page 40

catalyst A substance, such as an enzyme, that speeds up a reaction without itself being used up. Page 10 (biology), 29 (chemistry)

cell membrane The part of a cell that controls the entry and exit of materials. Page 2

cell sap The liquid that fills the vacuole in a plant cell. Page 2

cell wall The outer part of a plant cell, giving it shape and strength. Page 2

chain reaction Neutrons released when one nucleus splits then cause more nuclei to split, releasing further neutrons, and so on. Page 57

chloroplasts Part of a plant cell that contains chlorophyll. Page 2

chromosomes Long strands of genes made up of DNA. Page 15

clone A group of genetically identical cells. Page 15

closed system A reacting system is closed if none of the products can escape. Page 27

combustion Rapid oxidation causing heat to be released so rapidly that a substance burns. Page 31

compounds Atoms of two or more different elements chemically joined together to form a new substance with new properties. Page 20

conductor A material which allows an electric current to flow through it. Page 46

conserved Describes a quantity whose total amount remains constant during an event, e.g. momentum, energy. Page 44

controls The part of an experiment that shows that effects are due to changes in the independent variable. Page 4

coulomb (C) The unit of electric charge. Page 48

covalent bonds Chemical bonds formed when non-metals share electrons; molecules have covalent bonds. Page 22

covalent compound A compound formed when atoms from two or more elements are joined by covalent bonds. Page 23

current A flow of electric charge; the rate of flow of electric charge. Page 48

current–potential difference graph A graph showing how the current flowing through a component depends on the p.d. across it. Page 49

cystic fibrosis An inherited disease caused by a faulty recessive allele which causes excessive production of sticky mucus. Page 18

cytoplasm The part of the cell where many of the chemical reactions occur. These reactions are catalysed by enzymes. Page 2

Glossary and index

decay (organic) The breakdown of dead and waste material. Page 9

decay (radioactive) When a radioactive atom decays, it emits radiation and becomes a different type of atom. Page 55

denatured When an enzyme has changed shape so that the substrate no longer fits it and it no longer works. Page 10

detritus The dead remains of organisms. Page 6

diabetes Disorder where the pancreas fails to produce enough insulin to control blood glucose concentration. Page 14

differentiated cells Cells which are specialised to carry out a specific job in the body. Page 19

diffusion The movement of particles from a region of high concentration to a lower concentration. Page 3

digestion Breaking down large food molecules into smaller ones so that they can be absorbed. Page 11

diode A device which allows current to flow in one direction only. Page 50

direct current (d.c.) Current which flows in one direction only. Page 51

discharge A conductor can discharge electrostatic charge when a current flows from it to earth. Page 45

distance–time graph A graph showing how the distance travelled by an object depends on the time. Page 37

DNA (deoxyribose nucleic acid) A gene is a section of DNA. Page 15

dominant An allele which shows up in the phenotype when an organism is heterozygous or homozygous for it (see recessive). Page 17

earth The wire in a mains electricity supply whose voltage is always 0 V. Page 52

earthed Connected to the Earth by an electrical conductor, so a current can flow to earth. Page 46

elastic An elastic substance bounces back when it is compressed or stretched. Page 43

elastic potential energy Energy stored by an elastic object when it is stretched or squashed. Page 43

electrolysis The tearing apart of a molten (or dissolved) ionic compound using electricity. Page 34

electrons Particles much smaller than an atom, with tiny mass and a single negative charge. Electrons move through metals when a current flows. Page 20

electron shells The positions that electrons can occupy around an atom – same as energy levels. Page 20

electrostatic charge A property of some particles which causes them to attract or repel each other. Can be positive or negative. Page 46

element Substances made of one type of atom only. Page 20

endothermic A reaction that takes in energy. Page 31

energy levels The positions that electrons can occupy around an atom – same as electron shells. Page 20

enzyme Biological catalysts which speed up the rate of reactions taking place in and around cells. Page 10

equilibrium The balance point in a reversible reaction reached when the rates of the forward and back reactions are equal. Page 27

exothermic A reaction that gives out energy. Page 31

external force A force acting on an object or objects, caused by another object. Page 44

fluid Any substance which can flow; liquids and gases are fluids. Page 41

formula mass (M_r) The sum of the relative atomic masses of all the atoms in a compound (e.g. for water H_2O: $2 \times 1 + 16 = 18$). Page 25

frequency The number of waves per second; measured in hertz (Hz). Page 51

fuse A device containing a wire which melts when an excessive current flows through it, breaking the circuit. Page 52

gametes Specialised sex cells produced by meiosis. Page 16

gene Part of a chromosome which controls an inherited characteristic. Page 15

genetic diagram A diagram which shows the results of a genetic cross by showing the types of gametes produced and the results of fertilisation. Page 17

genetic screening Testing cells such as embryo cells for faulty alleles. Page 19

glucose A simple sugar produced by photosynthesis and from starch by digestion. Page 4

gravitational field strength The force of gravity acting on each kilogram of mass. Page 39

Haber process The industrial process used to make ammonia from nitrogen and hydrogen. Page 27

half equation   The reaction at one electrode in an electrolytic cell. Page 34

halide   An ionic compound of one of the halogens, such as chlorine. Page 22

halogen   A member of Group 7 of the periodic table, such as chlorine. Page 22

Huntington's disease   An inherited disease caused by a faulty dominant allele which damages the brain and other nerve tissue. Page 18

insulator   A material which does not readily conduct electricity but which can be charged with static electricity. Page 45

insulin   A hormone produced by the pancreas that controls the concentration of glucose in the blood. Page 13

intermolecular force   The weak force of attraction you get between uncharged molecules. Page 23

ionic bond   A bond formed by the electrostatic attraction between oppositely charged ions. Page 22

ionic compound   A compound formed by the electrostatic attraction between oppositely charged ions. Page 22

ions   Charged particles. Page 21

isotope   Atoms of an element come in different forms or isotopes, depending on the numbers of neutrons they have in their nuclei. Page 24

kinetic energy   The energy that an object has because it is moving. Page 42

lattice   The regular arrangement of particles in a crystal, for example. Page 22

light-dependent resistor (LDR)   A device whose resistance decreases when light shines on it. Page 50

limiting factor   A factor that limits the rate of a process. Page 5

lipase   A type of digestive enzyme which breaks fats and oils down into fatty acids and glycerol. Page 11

live   The wire in a mains electricity supply whose voltage varies most. Page 52

macromolecule   Giant structures where all the bonds are strong covalent bonds, such as diamond. Page 23

mass number (A)   The number of protons added to the number of neutrons in an atom. Page 24

meiosis   A form of cell division that reduces the number of chromosomes and results in variation. This type of cell division forms gametes. Page 16

microbe   Another word for microorganism. Page 9

microorganisms   Microscopic single-celled organisms. Many enzymes used in the home and in industry are obtained from microorganisms. Page 9

mitochondria   The part of a cell where most of the reactions in aerobic respiration occur. Page 2

mitosis   A form of cell division that forms cells identical to the parent cell. Page 15

model   An idea or picture of how something works. In science, we use models to help us explain ideas. Page 54

mole   The amount of a substance containing 6.02×10^{23} particles (e.g. the relative atomic mass or formula mass in grams). Page 25

molecules   Particles made from atoms joined by covalent bonds. Page 22

momentum   The quantity mass × velocity. Momentum has size and direction. Page 43

nanoparticles   Very small particles just a few tens of nanometres across or less. Page 23

nanotechnology   Technology based around the special properties of nanoparticles. Page 23

neutral   The wire in a mains electricity supply whose voltage is close to $0\,V$. Page 52

neutralisation   A chemical reaction between an acid and alkali (or base) that produces a neutral salt. Page 35

neutron   A sub-atomic particle with no electric charge and a relative mass of 1. Page 20

nitrates   Plants need these salts to make amino acids which are then built into protein. Page 5

noble gas   A gas from Group 0 of the periodic table, e.g. helium, argon, neon. Page 21

nuclear fission   When the nucleus of a massive atom splits into two smaller nuclei; energy is released. Page 56

nuclear fusion   When the nuclei of two small atoms join together to form a more massive nucleus; energy is released. Page 57

nuclear model   The picture of an atom with a tiny nucleus at its centre, and electrons orbiting it. Page 55

nucleus (atom)   The central part of the atom containing the proton(s) and, for all except hydrogen, the neutrons; has most of the mass of the atom. Page 20

nucleus (cell)   The part of a cell which contains genetic information. Page 2

ohm (Ω)   The unit of electrical resistance. Page 48

oscilloscope A device used to show the pattern of a rapidly changing voltage. Page 51

osmosis The net movement of water molecules through a partially permeable membrane from a region of high concentration of water molecules to a region of lower concentration. Page 3

oxidation Reaction with oxygen, e.g. iron is oxidised when iron oxide forms during rusting. Oxidation may also be defined as the loss of electrons. Page 34

parallel When electrical components are connected side by side. Page 49

percentage yield The actual yield as a percentage of the theoretical yield for a reaction. Page 26

pH scale A number scale to show the strength of acids or alkalis. 1 is the strongest acid, 7 is neutral, 14 is the strongest alkali. Page 35

photosynthesis A series of reactions in which plants use light energy to make sugars. Page 4

plum pudding model The picture of an atom as a sphere of positive charge with electrons embedded in it. Page 54

potential difference (p.d.) The voltage between two points which can make an electric current flow between them. Page 45

power The rate at which energy is transferred. Page 53

precipitate An insoluble solid that sometimes forms when two reacting solutions are mixed. Page 36

precipitator A device which uses static electricity to remove dust particles from the air in industrial equipment. Page 46

primary consumer An organism that eats plants. Page 6

producers Green plants that use light energy to make food. Page 6

properties What a material is like, e.g. melting point, hardness, strength etc. Page 23

protease A digestive enzyme that breaks down proteins into amino acids. Page 11

proton A sub-atomic particle with a positive charge and a relative mass of 1. Page 20

proton number Another name for the atomic number. Page 20

pyramid of biomass A diagram that shows the mass of living organisms at each stage in a food chain. Page 6

radioactive A radioactive material contains some atoms whose nuclei are unstable; these may spontaneously decay, giving out radiation. Page 55

rate of reaction How much reactant is used up (or product formed) divided by the time taken. Page 28

recessive An allele which shows in the phenotype only when an organism is homozygous for it (see dominant). Page 17

reduction The removal of oxygen from a compound, e.g. iron oxide is reduced to iron. Reduction may also be defined as the gain of electrons. Page 34

relative atomic mass (A_r) The mass of an atom compared to 1/12th of the mass of a carbon-12 atom. Page 24

reliable Evidence that can be reproduced by other experimenters. Page 18

resistance The greater the resistance of a component, the smaller the current that will flow through it for a given p.d. Page 48

resistor An electrical component whose resistance does not depend on the p.d. across it. Page 48

respiration A process which breaks down glucose to release energy for use by cells. Page 11

resultant force The unbalanced force when two or more forces act on an object. Page 39

ribosome The part of a cell where protein synthesis occurs. Page 2

salts Ionic compounds formed from positive ions (usually metallic) and negative ions from an acid. Page 35

secondary consumers An animal which eats animals that feed on plants. Page 6

series When electrical components are connected end-to-end. Page 48

specialised Each type of cell is adapted or specialised to its function. Page 2

speed The rate of change of distance. Page 37

starch The form of carbohydrate stored by most plants. Starch is made from glucose molecules joined together. Page 4

state symbols These symbols are often added to symbol chemical equations: (s) solid, (l) liquid, (g) gas, (aq) solution in water (aqueous solution). Page 35

static electricity Electricity which is not flowing as a current. Page 45

stem cell Cells, such as embryo cells, which can divide to form other types of cell. Page 19

stopping distance   The distance travelled by a vehicle between the time when the driver notices the need to stop and when the vehicle stops. Page 40

substrate   The molecules upon which an enzyme acts. Page 10

sustainable development   Development that conserves natural resources and so can be used successfully into the future. Page 26

terminal velocity   The top speed of an object falling through a fluid. Reached when friction balances gravity. Page 41

tertiary consumers   An animal which eats animals that feed on other animals. Page 6

thermistor   A device whose resistance decreases as its temperature increases. Page 50

thermoregulation   Maintaining a steady body temperature. Page 13

thinking distance   The distance travelled by a vehicle between the time when the driver notices the need to stop and when the brakes are applied. Page 40

universal indicator   An indicator that has a range of colours showing the strength of an acid or alkali on the pH scale. Page 35

vacuole   A fluid-filled sac found in most plant cells. Page 2

variable resistor   A resistor whose resistance may be altered to control the current flowing in a circuit. Page 50

variegated   A leaf which has green areas containing chlorophyll and yellow/white areas with no chlorophyll. Page 4

velocity   The speed of an object in a particular direction. Page 38

velocity–time graph   A graph showing how the velocity of an object depends on the time. Page 38

watt (W)   The unit of power; 1 watt is 1 joule per second. Page 53

weight   The downward force on an object caused by gravity. Page 39

work   Energy transferred by a force; work done = force × distance moved in the direction of the force. Page 42

yield   The amount of product you get; often expressed as a percentage of what is theoretically possible. Page 26